RAISING
NATURALLY
HEALTHY PETS

RAISING NATURALLY
HEALTHY PETS

A Guide to Helping Your Pets Live Longer

JUDY MORGAN DVM, CVA, CVCP, CVFT

Illustrated by Hue Grant

36 Paws Press

Published by 36 Paws Press

For more information, visit www.drjudymorgan.com

ISBN (paperback): 978-0-9972501-5-2
ISBN (ebook): 978-0-9972501-6-9

Book design by Christy Day, Constellation Book Services

Printed in the United States of America

This book is dedicated to all the animals that have been a part of my journey to learn as much as possible about keeping them healthy, happy, and engaged in life. They have given me more than I will ever be able to return; my heart is full of the joy they readily share.

Table of Contents

Introduction

When I wrote my first book *From Needles to Natural,* I had no idea it would transform my life and the lives of so many pets and pet parents around the world. Frankly, I was asked by a Cavalier King Charles Spaniel lovers Facebook group to write down some of my recommendations for diagnosis and treatment of common pet ailments, including alternative therapies that could be integrated with traditional medicine. I expected to sell a few hundred copies to friends and family. To my delight, the book grew into an internationally recognized reference manual for pet owners searching for answers. By the second year in production, I vowed to change the lives of one million pets worldwide. That has changed over time, with the current goal being to change the lives of ten million pets worldwide. I have learned to set lofty goals that are driven by my passion to improve longevity for our pets through healthy lifestyles.

In the 1970's the average life expectancy for a medium-size dog was seventeen years. Now, just a few decades later, those dogs are living an average of ten years. Over three-quarters of dogs living past age ten will develop cancer. These statistics are staggering. We have specialists in every field of veterinary medicine capable of keeping our pets alive longer, yet we are losing them earlier. We must make changes to how we feed, medicate, and treat our pets if we expect to change the numbers we are seeing.

By minimizing vaccinations to only those needed by individual pets, immune system function may be maintained instead of constantly being challenged and thrown into disarray. Elimination of harmful chemicals that destroy body systems and challenge liver and kidney metabolism allows the body to maintain healthy function. Feeding a diet that mimics what our pets would eat in the wild, using high-quality whole foods, supplies the nutrients needed to maintain good health, thereby increasing longevity. Feeding highly processed foods filled with dyes, sugars, salt, preservatives, and recycled waste products cannot possibly provide the ingredients necessary for supreme vitality.

My wish is that all pet dogs and cats could live well into their second and possibly third decades of life as our faithful companions, while maintaining good health. Over time, I firmly believe we can achieve this through better breeding, feeding, and health maintenance practices. First-time pet owners as well as seasoned professionals can learn more about caring for pets in a more natural manner that can improve health and longevity. Education is the key; this book, along with the other books and articles I and my colleagues have written, can help pet owners on their journey toward natural pet care.

Puppies and Kittens and New Additions

I s there anything more fun than welcoming a new furry addition into your home? They bring a spark of joy and laughter with their high-energy antics, often bringing renewed energy to older pets in the household. Personally, I am a big fan of senior pets, but that is mostly because our household is filled with senior citizens who enjoy a good nap by the fireplace. Over the past thirty-five years, I have brought home kittens and stray cats, bottle fed and kept kittens who lost their momma, adopted puppy mill breeding dogs, took in dogs surrendered by owners who could no longer care for them, and along the way even purchased a few dogs. There is no "right" or "wrong" way to add a pet to your home.

Recently, more people have started working from home and children are sometimes using remote learning instead of attending school. This has resulted in more families adopting or fostering dogs and cats. Over two thirds of households in America own at least one pet. Bringing a pet into your home is a huge responsibility. It means you are signing on for a lifetime of care that does not end when the pet becomes old and needs more intensive care or has more medical bills.

Getting these new pets started off on the right "paw" is critical. Diet, medical care, and training need to be taken into consideration to ensure a long, happy life. It is never too late to set your pet onto a better path, even if they come to you with a long list of health or behavioral issues.

Choosing the Right Pet

Many puppies, kittens, and rescue animals are brought into the home without a lot of planning before-hand. I hear stories all the time: "I just stopped in the pet store to look—I had no intentions of bringing one home!" "I just stopped at the shelter to drop off old towels—I had no intention of walking past the forlorn faces pleading to come with me, let alone bring one home!" "I saw that face online and I just could not resist…"

There are some folks out there who do in-depth research and planning before adopting a pet. I applaud these efforts; however, many times, thorough consideration of several factors is not taken. If you are a planner (or aspire to be one!), the following would be great to consider when researching the correct pet for your household:

- How much exercise will the pet need? Would you prefer a high-energy breed or a more sedentary lap pet?
- Will you need a fenced yard?
- Will you need to walk the pet outside multiple times per day?
- Who will be walking the pet? What size pet can they handle?
- Does the pet need to be good with children?
- Will the pet be able to get along with other pets already in the household?
- What are the costs for feeding and medical care, both now and as an adult? Large breed dogs can be expensive to feed, especially if you plan to feed very-high-quality meals. Medications cost more for larger dogs. Senior pets may have more medical expenses.
- Can you handle a pet with disabilities?
- What is your lifestyle? Would adopting a senior pet make more sense?
- Can you afford the necessary medical treatments that may come up? Plan on a minimum of $500 to $1,000 per year, with bills in the thousands should an unplanned emergency arise.
- If you rent or live in a community, are there limits on size, number, type, or breed of pet?
- Does anyone have allergies? Do you need to find a non-shedding breed?
- Are you committed to caring for a pet for two decades, no matter the costs or the types of care required?
- Do you know how to train the pet you are considering? How will you deal with behavior problems? Behavior problems are the number one reason pets are surrendered to shelters.

- Do you need a pet that will not require regular trips to a groomer?
- Do you prefer a male or a female? I have gone back and forth on this one over the years. I can say at this point it really does not matter; I love them all.
- Do you have the time needed to socialize and interact with a pet?
- How many hours per day will the pet be left alone?
- Are you willing to care for the pet when your children who have begged for the pet are no longer interested in caring for it?
- Are you willing to feed a species-appropriate diet? If you are not willing to feed a meat-based diet to a dog or cat, I strongly recommend adopting an herbivore such as a rabbit or guinea pig.
- How will you react if the pet destroys a piece of furniture or woodwork?
- Can you handle cleaning a litterbox and mess associated with litter tracking?

Once you have decided on the appropriate species, breed, size, and temperament you will have to decide whether you want to try to find a reputable breeder or try to rescue from one of the thousands of rescue agencies. Both processes can be a bit challenging. Many backyard breeders, puppy mill breeders, and low-quality breeders advertise online with websites that make the pets sound like purebred champions from champion lines, when they are poorly bred with no regard to genetic superiority.

Most of our dogs have come from puppy mill rescues and our cats were bottle-fed kittens from animal shelter mommas or kittens born to feral cats who arrived at our farm. While they were not bred for superior genetics, they have all been wonderful pets and I would adopt each one of them again. We also have dogs bred by reputable breeders for the showring that developed medical issues that made them no longer suitable for breeding. Removing them from the breeding lines was the ethical choice made by those breeders.

If you are concerned with costs and emotions that might arise from poor breeding, you would be better off finding a breeder that performs genetic testing and can give some guarantees of good and lasting health, free from genetic diseases. Of course, there are no guarantees and I have had clients pay thousands of dollars for dogs with good breeding that still developed heritable diseases. A good breeder will stand by the pet, offering reimbursement for some of the medical fees, at least up to the sale price paid for the pet. Good breeders stay in touch with owners who purchased from them because they want to know if any medical issues have developed that would eliminate a breeding pair from their program.

Heritable conditions vary between breeds. There are good books and online resources that list problems you should investigate. Good resources include:

- www.instituteofcaninebiology.org/genetic-disorders-by-breed.html
- www.catvirus.com/breeds.htm
- Wisdom Panel and Embark are two DNA testing kits that are simple to use to test your dog for genetic disorders.
- BasePaws Cat is an option for feline genetic testing.

This information can be useful when questioning a potential breeder about possible disorders in their breeding line.

3

New Pet Shopping List

Pets are expensive. Adopting or buying a new pet should not be taken lightly. Be sure your budget can accommodate the needs of your new addition; do not forget to include funding for veterinary care and emergency care should something happen. Items you may want to include on your list:

- Collar—can be used to hold identification tags or can be embroidered with name and phone number. Cat collars should have a quick-release buckle or mechanism.
- Leash—retractable leashes are not safe and are not recommended; a sturdy 6-foot leash is best for dogs. A lightweight but sturdy leash is best for cats.
- Harness—should fit well and not rub. Cat harnesses are also available in different sizes.

- Bed (s)—type will depend on the size of the pet.
- Crate for home—useful for sleeping and housetraining.
- Crate or bag for transport—particularly for small dogs and cats; top-load crates or bags are easiest to get pets into.
- Food and water bowls—stainless steel is best, avoid plastic as it may cause allergic reactions in some pets. Feeding on a flat platter is preferable over a bowl. The Mine Pet Platter is made of cellulose which is nonallergenic and sturdy. The science behind feeding pets can be found at https://minepetplatter.com/p/the-platter
- Identification tags—flat tags that attach to the collar and will not make noise or dangle are best. I am a fan of https://www.boomerangtags.com/
- Brushes—multiple types may be needed, depending on coat type. A slicker brush is a good all-purpose brush; a curry brush works well for dogs with short hair.
- Comb—A medium-toothed comb is a good all-around comb. I like the combs with teeth that rotate so the hair does not pull when there are tangles.
- Shampoo—natural, essential oil shampoos without sulfates and detergents are best. Do not use human shampoo or bathing products on pets.
- Conditioner—particularly useful for long-haired breeds; natural essential oil products are best.
- Nail trimmers and styptic powder—Dremel or clippers, whichever you are more comfortable using; use the powder if a nail is accidentally clipped too short.
- Car restraints—pets, like children, should be restrained for their safety and yours.
- Toys—size and toughness will depend on the size and breed of the pet.

- Treats—organic, natural, minimal ingredient are best.
- Food—see Chapter 20—"Choosing the Right Diet for Your Pet."
- Dental products—toothbrush and dental products. See Chapter 22—"Dental Care".
- Training pads or litter box, scoop, and litter—disposable or reusable training pads can be used for dogs; size and choice of litter will vary according to size and breed of cat. See Chapter 9—"Potty Training Dogs & Cats".
- Pooper scooper and poop bags for collecting waste.
- Gates or fencing—useful to block off areas of the home until the pet is house trained and trustworthy; temporary exercise pens are easy to set up in the yard if you do not have a fenced yard.
- Scratching post for kitties—should have multiple surface types on the post.
- Cat tree or cat beds for sleeping.
- Enzyme cleaner for "accidents"—they are bound to happen; better to be prepared!
- Clothing—this is totally up to you. Some pets love to wear sweaters or coats, others will not tolerate them.
- Pet insurance—this can be a game-changer in an emergency or when a pet needs surgery.

Pet Insurance

Injuries can happen at any time, usually when you are least prepared to take on a large veterinary bill. Most pet owners will spend $2,000 to $5,000 on at least one emergency procedure or hospitalization during the life span of the pet. Pet insurance can help offset some or most of the costs of paying a veterinarian to diagnose, treat, and manage a pet's illness or injury. And this insurance could help avoid having to choose "economic euthanasia"—letting a beloved animal go because you cannot afford that big bill.

Currently, only 1% of pets are covered by pet insurance in the United States. Studies show that owners with pet insurance are more likely to obtain veterinary care for their pets.

Pet plans include deductibles, copays, and monthly premiums, and have coverage limitations. You will be responsible to cover the bills yourself and wait for reimbursement. Unlike in human medicine, veterinary offices do not submit billing to insurance companies. The upside to this is that there are no limitations on which veterinarian you use, as there are no "out of network" providers.

Decide whether you want coverage for preventive and routine care or only illness and accident. Most insurance companies will require a physical examination by a veterinarian to determine whether there are any pre-existing conditions that might not be covered in the future. Ask if there are limitations on the amount of coverage per incident or over the lifetime of the pet.

If you want to include holistic or alternative care in your pet's therapies, be sure to ask if acupuncture, chiropractic, cold laser therapy, physical therapy, and regenerative therapies are included in coverage. You should also ask if genetically predisposed diseases will be covered for your pet breed.

The average accident and illness premiums currently cost $585 per year for a dog and $350 for a cat, but the costs rise depending on your pet's breed (purebreds cost more to insure because they are more susceptible to some hereditary conditions), age (plans usually cost more annually as your pet ages), ZIP code (the higher cost of veterinary care in some areas is factored into your premium), and the coverage you choose. Medical treatment for dogs is usually more expensive than for cats. Some plans limit coverage to "usual and customary costs" based on veterinary pricing in your area.

If you are considering a policy, look for free quotes, terms and conditions, and a sample policy on insurers' websites. Consider coverage with simple, percentage-based payouts and no reliance on judgments of what's "reasonable," to avoid your own future headaches. Find out how your premiums might increase as your pet ages.

While you may not get the most bang for your buck with a

relatively healthy pet, there is no way to predict what illnesses or injuries might occur, and for many pet owners, knowing they have a safety net in place is valuable enough. Catastrophic coverage with a higher deductible may be more affordable and give enough coverage when needed in a crisis.

An alternative to pet insurance would be setting up your own health savings account for your pet. Contribute money monthly to build an account that can be used in an emergency. If you are apt to borrow money from the account to cover other expenses, this will do no good in the event of a large veterinary bill.

When I was in practice, some of my clients put money on their account every month for use at their annual visit or in case of an illness or emergency. This works well if you might be tempted to borrow from your pet's emergency fund.

5

Finding the Right Veterinarian

Preferably, you should choose your veterinarian before buying or adopting a new pet. If you do not already have a working relationship with a veterinarian you like, researching before obtaining a new pet is important. New puppies, kittens, and adopted pets are under a lot of emotional and immune stress when they are taken away from their mother, littermates, foster home, or shelter. Animals that have spent time in a shelter environment have been enduring stress for the length of time they were there. While you may be the most loving, wonderful pet parent ever imagined, you still are new to them, and they will be moving to a new environment that can be strange and intimidating.

Stress of re-homing and separation from the litter or pack can lead to an outbreak of upper respiratory illness, diarrhea, or loss of appetite. Parasite infestations may become problematic as the immune system struggles to handle disease. Having a veterinarian onboard will make your life much easier when you call with a problem that must be dealt with immediately.

If you are searching for a holistic veterinarian, your best resource may be www.AHVMA.org in the United States. Check www. holisticvet.co.uk and www.bhma.org in the UK. In Australia, www. ahvets.com.au has a searchable page. For other countries, search online for holistic veterinarians. Unfortunately, not all veterinarians listed as holistic truly practice holistic medicine. Many still promote over-vaccination and use of harmful chemicals and prescription diets sourced from poor quality ingredients. You will have to visit the office to determine their philosophies on diet, vaccination, and parasite prevention. Sometimes you can find one veterinarian who is holistic within a traditional practice, so do not count them out just because you see prescription diets lining shelves in the waiting or reception area.

The goal is to find a veterinarian you like and trust, one who will listen to your concerns and be willing to have conversations without giving you the eye roll. Traditional veterinarians can be very open to discussing modified vaccine schedules and while they may not promote feeding raw or home-prepared meals, they may be willing to kindly agree to disagree. Sometimes that is the best you can hope for, particularly if you live in a remote area with limited access to veterinary care.

Be sure you understand the hours the practice is open and where you will need to go if an emergency should arise with your pet. Searching for the closest veterinarian when your pet is in crisis will delay care that needs to be provided. Keep emergency information in your phone or posted somewhere within easy sight.

If the practice has a website, that is a good first start. Read the bios on the veterinarians and staff as well as services the practice offers. You can also talk to family, friends, and neighbors in the area to see if they use a practice that they would recommend.

Determine how far you are willing to travel to see a well-recommended doctor. Some pets travel well, while others may be stressed during travel and would be better off going to a local practice or having a house-call veterinarian come to your home.

Once you decide which veterinary practice you would like to use, set up an appointment (by phone or in person) to meet with the doctor and discuss the future care for your new addition. Be willing to pay for the time the doctor devotes to this interview. If you would like to feed a non-traditional diet or limit vaccinations, it is best to have that conversation ahead of time, so you will not feel pressured when you arrive with your new pet. Ask which vaccinations they recommend and how often they should be given. If the veterinarian has a "one-size-fits-all" vaccination approach, ask if they are willing to give fewer vaccines based on the lifestyle of your pet. If you want to feed raw or home-prepared meals, ask the veterinarian if they will support you in that endeavor. Many veterinarians will argue that raw or home-prepared food is detrimental to your pet and your family; this can be a point of contention if your views differ from theirs. If there are multiple doctors in the practice, ask if you can request a doctor you like for your regular appointments.

Your pet should have a complete physical examination and routine blood tests at least once per year before age seven, increasing to twice a year when they are getting older. This is the time to have any new lumps, bumps, or areas of concern addressed. Make a list of questions prior to the exam so you are well prepared and sure to get all your questions answered. A good resource for making your list of questions is my veterinary visit checklist. The form is available as a free download on www.drjudymorgan.com.

PREPARING FOR A VETERINARY VISIT

I recommend taking stool and urine samples with you to all appointments, particularly if your pet is ill. If not needed, they can be thrown away; it is better to be prepared. Samples should be obtained within twelve hours of the visit and stored in the refrigerator until they are submitted. A tablespoon each of urine and stool is enough for testing. Place them in clean containers that can be sealed for transport.

Note whether you want any vaccinations given at the visit. Be VERY SPECIFIC. I recommend that only ONE vaccine be given per visit, not multiple vaccines. Vaccines should not be given if the pet is sick!

Be very clear if you do NOT want any vaccinations given at the visit. BE VERY SPECIFIC AND HIGHLIGHT THIS.

Note that you want a doctor to call or speak with you before ANY treatments are started, after they perform a complete physical exam. Ask for an estimate prior to performance of any diagnostic testing or treatments.

Ask for an estimate for any recommendations for future procedures (surgery, dental care, etc.)

VETERINARY VISIT CHECKLIST
(This can also be downloaded at
www.drjudymorgan.com)

APPOINTMENT INFORMATION:

Date:

Time:

Phone number to reach me during the appointment
(if you cannot go in with your pet or need to have
someone else take your pet to the appointment):

PLEASE CALL ME BEFORE PERFORMING ANY PRO-
CEDURES OTHER THAN THE PHYSICAL EXAM.

I WOULD LIKE AN ESTIMATE FOR ALL PROCEDURES
BEFORE THEY ARE PERFORMED.

OWNER'S INFORMATION

Name:

Address:

Home phone number:

Email address:

Make and color of vehicle I am in (if you are doing
curbside check in):

PET INFORMATION:

Name:

Species: (dog or cat or other)

Breed:

Color:

Age:

Sex: (neutered, spayed, or intact?)

Past medical issues or allergies:

Current Diet: (type, brand, protein base, frequency, and amount you are feeding)

Current Supplements:

Current Medications:

REASON FOR VISIT

My pet is coming to see you today because: (include symptoms and how long they have been going on)

Vaccinations I would like to be given today:

Tests I would like performed today: I WOULD LIKE TO SPEAK TO THE DOCTOR FIRST (circle, highlight, or cross out)

- ☐ CBC
- ☐ Chemistry Screen
- ☐ Thyroid Screen
- ☐ Urinalysis
- ☐ Fecal Exam
- ☐ Vaccine titers
- ☐ Heartworm test
- ☐ Tick disease testing

- ☐ Specialty testing: (for instance, test for Cushing's disease, Addison's disease, feline viral diseases...)
- ☐ X-rays (which body parts?)

Treatments I would like performed today: (things like fluid therapy, injections, acupuncture, laser, chiropractic treatment, bandaging, wound care, etc.)

SPEAK TO ME BEFORE PERFORMING THESE PLEASE.

- ☐ My pet's appetite is: (normal, eating less, eating more than usual)
- ☐ My pet's water consumption is: (normal, less, or more than usual)
- ☐ My pet's urination is: (normal, less, or more than usual) Any accidents in the house? Any blood noted?
- ☐ My pet has/has not recently changed weight: (gained, loss, how much, duration)
- ☐ My pet has/has not been vomiting or has/has not had diarrhea: (If yes, describe how often, how long after eating, how long it has been going on, if there is any blood or mucous, if this has happened in the past, color, consistency)
- ☐ My pet has/has not had coughing or sneezing or runny eyes or nose: (If yes, describe frequency, severity, discharge color and consistency from eyes, nose, or mouth)
- ☐ My pet has been scratching, rubbing the face, rubbing the ears or eyes: (yes or no, duration)

☐ There is a bad odor or discharge coming from my pet: (ears, eyes, mouth, wound, anal glands)— describe length of time, where you suspect it is coming from.

☐ My pet is/is not painful. (symptoms, duration, location of pain):

☐ My pet's behavior has/has not changed: (hiding, restless, panting more, pacing, up at night, vocalizing)

☐ My pet has/has not gotten into or eaten anything unusual recently (trash, diapers, mulch, other pet's food, medications, etc.):

☐ My pet spends time outside supervised/unsupervised (choose one or both). Amount of time spent outside:

☐ Recent environmental changes within the household: (new babies, new pets, visitors, people moving in or out)

Other concerns about my pet: (fearful, does not like men/women, needs a muzzle, does not like having his feet touched, etc.)

An annual exam is a time when your veterinarian will want to discuss vaccinations that they consider necessary. Please read Chapter 15 on vaccines and consider your pet's individual lifestyle, rather than accepting a "one-size-fits-all" plan that includes many vaccines that are not necessary for your pet. If you determine that multiple vaccines will be needed, split the vaccines between multiple visits rather than having them given all at once as this is a major stress on the immune system. Immune stress can lead to chronic inflammatory diseases and allergies.

A stool sample should be examined microscopically for parasites. Parasite prevention and treatment will be covered in Chapter 16. Blood should be drawn to test how the internal organs are functioning. Even young animals should have a baseline complete blood count, chemistry panel, urinalysis, and stool test. Knowing what is "normal" for your pet can be valuable information when they are sick so that you have laboratory results for comparison. You should ask for copies of all laboratory tests; keep them in a file, notebook, or electronic file for easy reference.

During the examination, the whole animal should be examined: otoscopic examination of ears, oral exam to check for tartar and gingivitis, ophthalmoscopic eye exam, auscultation (stethoscope) of both lungs and all heart valves, abdominal palpation, flexion and extension of all limb joints, examination of coat and skin, palpation of lymph nodes, and a check of the region under the tail. A rectal exam should be performed if there is any concern regarding prostate enlargement, anal gland, or rectal problems. Be sure your pet is weighed so you can document gain or loss over time.

It is not unreasonable to request a copy of the physical examination notes for your records. This is easier for clinics that do everything electronically, but any clinic should be able to make copies. If you keep copies of laboratory and examination notes you will have everything handy in the event of an emergency trip to a veterinarian who is not familiar with your pet.

The physical examination should not be a few words stating, "all normal". Each organ system should be documented. Holding your veterinarian accountable for writing all exam findings will ensure a thorough physical examination is performed. Vaccines and treatments should not be performed unless the animal has had a recent complete examination to determine any changes in health that might change the treatment plan.

Socialization

Socialization is not necessarily about learning to be social. Think of it as exposure therapy, teaching your pet to remain calm in different scenarios to help them overcome any anxiety and build confidence. Animals that are well socialized are less likely to react with fear or aggression when faced with new situations.

For dogs, desensitizing them to different environments is key. If you live in an urban city, the dog will be exposed to loud trucks, cars, and sirens. If you live in the suburbs, the dog will need to become familiar with things such as bicycles, deer, or even grass. Animals adopted from puppy mills are not familiar with grass— this may seem odd, but they have never seen grass! The more environments the dog experiences, the easier it will be to travel with him or her in the future.

Cats should also be socialized with frequent handling and

grooming. Leave the cat carrier that will be used for transportation out in the open where the cat can climb in or on top. Place a soft towel or bed and some treats in the carrier. Training the cat to associate the carrier with positive experiences will decrease stress when you need to transport your kitty.

Both cats and dogs should be trained to ride in the car early in life. I adopted my first kitten when he was only six weeks old. He had two broken legs with his entire hind end in a plaster cast (we still used plaster in 1984). Puff had to have his cast changed every ten to fourteen days because he was a growing boy which meant he had to ride over an hour each way in the car to go to work with me. He loved riding in the car and never howled or carried on like my other cats have been known to do.

Physical touch is also important. Touching paws, ears, and the mouth will make nail trims, ear cleaning, and dental care much easier if the pet has no fear when being handled.

The ideal window for socialization is between eight and twelve weeks of age because the brain is still developing, making dogs and cats receptive to learning new behaviors. While the socialization window will have closed if you adopt an older animal, it is never too late to desensitize those animals. Use positive reinforcement training only. This will help your pet be set up for success for the rest of their lives.

While it is tempting to take your new family member out and about to meet all your friends, relatives, and neighbors, please remember that being handled by many people and introduced to new places will be challenging to the little one. Imagine being very, very small in a world of large beings with loud noises, bright colors, and many new faces. It can be overwhelming and lead to immune stress and illness.

Take your time introducing your new pet, limiting meetings to small groups and quiet animals that are healthy. This is not the time to take your pet shopping at a big box store or to large pet events that are noisy and filled with pets of unknown background.

If possible, pick up your new puppy, kitten, or adopted pet early in the day and plan on spending the day introducing your pet to the new surroundings in your home. If you are planning to keep the pet in one part of the house, make sure you have everything set up to ease the transition. Have plenty of natural cleaning supplies on hand for the accidents that are all but guaranteed to occur.

If there are other pets in the home, introduce each one individually. Watch closely for any signs of fear or aggression such as curled lips, growling, fur raised, rigid back, ears flat, tucked tails, or cowering, so you can intervene if necessary. Pets already in the home may become territorial or protective of their humans, toys, food, and other possessions. Until you are sure everyone will get along, it is best to err on the side of caution.

Allowing dogs to meet outside on a walk may be a gentle way to introduce newcomers. Using gates to separate rooms, allowing animals to sniff and greet without having to physically interact, can be a great way to let them get used to the idea they will be cohabitating. Cats may need to be separated on opposite sides of a door, allowing them to smell each other under the door. Be sure each cat has a litter box, bed, and toys of their own, as they can be very territorial. If bringing a cat into a household of dogs, be sure the dogs do not have a high prey-drive. Cats and dogs can be best friends when introduced correctly.

If pets are having a hard time adjusting to a new environment or new additions to the household, to ease their transition consider using:

- Flower essences—Aspen, Larch, Honeysuckle, Elm, Rock Water, and Walnut flowers are options. There are combination pet essences also available, such as Botanical Animal, Blackwing Farms, and Animal Rx.

- Homeopathic remedies for anxiety (Nat mur, Ignatia amara, Aconitum napellus).
- Calming music—Through a Dog's Ear and Through a Cat's Ear are two options.
- Essential oils—Lavender, Ylang, Bergamot, and Chamomile work well. Use only oils approved for animals. Cats are more sensitive to side effects with some oils; always check safety before using. AnimalEO is a veterinary-owned company that produces high quality oils safe for all animals.
- Pheromone diffusers, sprays, and collars—Adaptil for dogs and Feliway for cats are two options.
- Anxiety wraps—Thundershirt, Mellow Shirt, ZenPet, AKC Calming Coat, Happy Hoodie, Surf City Pet Works, and Healer's Anxiety are a few examples.

Various remedies are available online from reputable sources. Never use remedies, oils, or any products not approved for use in animals. Cats are more sensitive to these products than dogs, so do your research before using anything new.

Crate Training

While many people view using a crate as a punishment or cruelty, I think crates are very important tools, especially for puppies or rescue pets that have never been in a home environment. No one would consider leaving an infant or toddler unsupervised in a home; animals are no different. Far too many animals are harmed from chewing on electrical cords, getting into foods or medications that are toxic, and falling from stairs or heights. Until your new addition learns what may be safely chewed, your furniture, walls, shoes, toys, and clothing are fair game. It is up to you to consistently teach them right from wrong.

Crate training can also be very useful for traveling in the car and staying in hotels or other homes. Knowing your pet is safely contained and cannot be destructive brings peace of mind. It also allows the pet to feel at home in an environment that is familiar.

We use crates any time we travel. Cats that have been crate trained are much less stressed during travel for veterinary visits, grooming, boarding, or vacation.

Kittens can be just as destructive, chewing cords, getting tangled in window blinds, and using inappropriate areas for potty time. While most people do not consider crating kittens while they are away at work, it is not a bad idea to confine them to a safe area when they are not supervised until they learn the rules of the home.

I have heard many owners state they felt bad the pet rescued from a breeding mill has spent their entire life in a crate and based on that, they feel it would be cruel to ever put them in a crate again. I can say with certainty that most of my puppy mill rescue dogs sought out a crate as a place of refuge. They understood it as their home for many years; it made them feel secure to be confined. I generally allow the door to remain open, but they have the option of retreating to a crate any time they want security.

A crate should be treated as a den or bedroom for the pet, not as punishment or time out. Going into the crate should be a pleasant experience. Dogs are maternal den animals by nature, which makes training easier. The crate teaches the dog responsibility and independence in a safe environment. The crate should be big enough for the dog to stand up, turn around, and lie comfortably on its side. Blankets or pads should only be placed in the crate if you know the pet will not chew them. While you do want them to have a soft bed, you do not want to go through the fiasco of foreign body surgery if bedding is eaten and swallowed. My last Doberman puppy could not have a bed until he was eighteen months old. He shredded everything!

It is easiest to train the dog as a puppy, placing treats inside the crate and allowing him to chew or relax with the door left open. Place high-value rewards inside to encourage him to go in on his own, followed with lots of praise. Eventually you will be able to close the door and leave him inside for short periods of time, gradually increasing as he tolerates it. Older dogs can be trained to use crates by using these same methods. This same practice can be used for cats to teach them their crate is not a bad place used only for those horrible trips to the veterinarian.

Dogs and cats inherently do not want to soil the area where they sleep. If the pet is not left for extended periods of time in the crate, they will do their best to keep the area clean. Using a crate generally makes house training much easier. However, I have had more trouble with puppy mill rescue dogs that have spent most of their life in a crate. They are used to soiling in the crate since they have never had access to anything else. Most of our mill rescue dogs have done very well being trained to washable, reusable piddle pads, as they do not recognize grass outside as a place to potty.

Never leave collars or harnesses on the dog or cat in the crate. Too many pets have been choked by getting the collar caught, unable to free themselves.

Crates come in wire, plastic, or cloth. Choosing the right crate will depend on your individual situation. Wire crates allow for more air flow and allows the pet to see everything around him. Many wire crates fold flat for easier storage and moving; most also come with divider panels that allow you to adjust the size of the cage if you have a growing pup or kitten. Many also feature a sliding tray bottom for easy cleanup. Disadvantages of wire crates include the possibility of getting paws or toes trapped in gaps.

Plastic crates are generally lighter weight than metal crates; most can be popped apart for storage, however they do not fold flat. The bottoms of most plastic crates can also be used as beds. Plastic crates have holes to allow the pet to see out, but the view is limited, which may block potential distractions. Many plastic crates are also airline-approved if you are planning to travel. Some pets may feel too isolated in a plastic crate. Air circulation in a hot environment can be a problem with these confined crates.

Cloth crates are not as strong as wire or plastic and can be chewed or destroyed by digging claws. They do fold flat and are lightweight for transport and storage. Cloth crates can be more difficult to keep clean and odor-free.

8

Potty Training

DOGS

House-training requires patience, commitment, and lots of consistency. Accidents are part of the process. If you adopted an adult dog that is soiling in the house, the dog may never have been house trained, may have lived outside or in a puppy mill cage, may be dealing with separation anxiety, or may even be afraid of going outside. It is important to rule out medical problems in addition to behavioral problems if you have trouble getting your dog trained. Be sure to have a thorough physical examination by your veterinarian, along with laboratory testing including stool and urine testing.

Establish a routine; like babies, pets do best on a regular schedule. The schedule teaches them that there are times to eat, times to play, and times to do their business. Generally, a puppy can control its bladder one hour for every month of age. So, if your puppy is two months old, he or she can hold it for about two hours. Do not go longer than this between bathroom breaks or your pup is likely to have an accident. Take the puppy outside frequently—at least every two hours—and immediately after waking up, during and after playing, and after eating or drinking.

Pick a bathroom spot outside; each time you take the dog out, go to that spot. While your dog is relieving himself, use a specific word or phrase that you can eventually use before he goes to remind him what to do. Take him out for a longer walk or some playtime only after he has eliminated. Avoid distractions with toys or other pets during potty time.

Reward your puppy every time he or she eliminates outdoors. Praise or give treats—but remember to do so immediately after he has finished, not after he comes back inside. This step is vital, because rewarding your dog for going outdoors is the only way to teach what is expected of him. Before rewarding, be sure he is finished. Puppies are easily distracted and if you praise too soon, he may forget to finish until he is back in the house.

Put your dog on a regular feeding schedule. What goes into a dog on a schedule comes out of a dog on a schedule. Depending on their age, puppies usually need to be fed three or four times a day. Feeding your puppy at the same times each day will make it more likely that the pup will eliminate at consistent times as well, making housetraining easier for both of you.

Do not give your dog an opportunity to soil in the house; always watch your pet while inside the house. You can tether your dog to you or a nearby piece of furniture within your sight with a six-foot leash if you are not actively training or playing. Watch for signs that your dog needs to go out. Some signs are obvious, such as barking or scratching at the door, squatting, restlessness, sniffing around or circling. Hanging bells or a tambourine on the doorknob within nose-reach of the dog can be helpful for training. Ring the bells each time you take the dog outside and soon your pet will learn to ring them when he needs to go outside. When you see these signs, immediately grab the leash, and take your dog outside to the bathroom spot. If poop or pee happens, reward with praise. Give your dog some freedom in the house and yard only after he becomes reliably housetrained. Remember that when it comes to housetraining, prevention is the key.

Scolding a dog for soiling your rug, especially after the fact, is not going to do anything except confuse the dog. Likewise, some old methods of punishment, like rubbing a dog's nose in its poop, are so bizarre that it is hard to imagine how they came to be and if they ever worked for anyone. On the other hand, praising a puppy for doing the right thing works best for everything you will do in your life together. Make your dog think he is a little canine genius every time this simple, natural act is performed.

If your dog has an accident do not overreact; just clean up the mess. A cleaner that also kills odors will remove the scent so the dog will not use that area in the future. House cleaning products often contain ammonia, which can make the smell worse. This means you need to use a cleaner specifically made for pet accidents. I like enzyme and essential oil products. When your dog urinates or defecates inside, clean up the mess first. Throw any feces away in a sealed bag and soak up as much urine as you can with disposable or washable towels. Clean the spot once with the cleanser, working it into the carpet or flooring. Rinse the area well and then add a mixture of water and baking soda. Rinse again and dry any additional moisture. An enzymatic cleaner may eliminate this step.

Most dogs can be trained within a few weeks, no matter the age. I have found the process to be more difficult for those coming from puppy mill situations, as they have never had the opportunity to urinate and defecate outside. Grass is an unfamiliar substance.

Sometimes it is easier to train them to eliminate on disposable or reusable piddle pads. All our dogs have been taught to use pads, as well as going outside.

CAT LITTER BOX TRAINING

One of the great things about kittens is that most will instinctively start using a litter box by about three to four weeks of age. It is natural for them to want to scratch and bury their urine and feces. Make sure the litter box is easy to find, yet out of the main flow of traffic in the house. It may be easiest to confine the kitten or cat to the room containing the litter box for the first few days so there is no mistaking where to find it.

For very small kittens or senior cats, it may be beneficial to have a litter box with lower sides to make it easier to climb in and out. Many senior cats have arthritis and may avoid the box because they have trouble getting over the edge of the box. Do not punish the kitten or cat that misses the box. They will not know why you are mad, which may cause them to hide and avoid the room with the litter box.

It is recommended to have a litter box on each level of the house if you have multiple floors. Particularly for kittens or cats that may have loose stools or urinary urgency, running up or down multiple flights of stairs may take too long to get to the box. Be sure to place the boxes in a quiet area where dogs and children will not bother the cat in the box.

Make sure the litter boxes are not too close to the feeding station. Cats do not like to have their bathroom and kitchen close together.

If multiple cats live in the household, it is recommended to have one more box than the number of cats. Sometimes each cat will claim one box they like; some cats will not use a soiled box. The boxes should be cleaned twice a day, every day. Consider how you would feel using an unflushed toilet that has been sitting for days. I use clumping litter that is easy to clean. By scooping stool and urine clumps twice a day, the cats never have to use a dirty box. The number one reason cats avoid the box is because it is dirty.

Make sure the litter box is big enough for the cat. It should be about one and a half times the length of their body. Large cats will urinate or defecate over the sides of the box if it is not big enough. I do not recommend enclosed boxes. Benefits include privacy for the cat, but some cats feel too confined and will not use them. Enclosed boxes with clear lids may help solve the confinement issue, as the cat can see anyone approaching the area.

If your cat soils outside the box, clean the area with an enzymatic cleaner to remove any odors that might attract the cat back to that area. After cleaning, put a couple of treats down; cats do not like to urinate or defecate where they eat. Block off the area if possible or cover it with plastic wrap or tin foil. Cats do not like to urinate on these surfaces. If your cat is using your indoor potted plants as a litter box, foil works well as a deterrent.

Choosing the litter for the box can involve trial and error. I do not recommend scented litters. Remember that a cat's sense of smell is much more sensitive than ours; many cats find the artificial scents offensive. I am not a fan of clay litters with large pieces, as walking on these can be painful for cats. The more finely ground litters are better for clumping but may track more outside the box.

There are many variations of litter that are available. Some cats are very picky and will not use litter with certain textures or smells. Types of kitty litter include:

- Clumping litter—When the cat urinates the litter forms into a firm, scoopable clump. This litter is usually a fine, sand-type consistency that can be carried on the fur and feet, causing more tracking throughout the house, however this does make the litter box easier to clean. Placing mats around the box to collect most of the debris from the cat leaving the box can be helpful.

- Non-Clumping litter—This litter tends to be less expensive, however it does need to be replaced more often than clumping litter, so may be no more cost effective in the long run. The urine is soaked into the litter instead of forming a clump, so the entire box must be changed at least weekly.

- Crystals—These are a great choice for avoiding dust and decreasing tracking. However, crystals can stick to the cat's paws and be ingested during grooming. There are non-stick options available. This is a great option for cats or people with asthma, as there is no dust.

- Recycled paper pellets—Some people love these; others say they do not cover odors well enough. Not all cats like the larger pellets. The pellets can be composted.

- Corn—This is natural, biodegradable, and earth-friendly. Some cats may be allergic to it. Watch for sores on the hind legs and feet.

- Coconut husks—Another natural, compostable litter.

- Wheat—The starch inside the wheat kernels is clumping and neutralizes odors. Some cats may be allergic to it. Watch for sores on the hind legs and feet.

- Wood—Natural, compostable product, may be pine scented depending on product used.

- Walnut shells—natural, compostable, available in clumping and non-clumping forms.

- Soil or sand—natural, clean soil or sand can work well for cats that are having trouble learning to use the box, as this is what they would find in nature. Odor control is problematic.

- ☻ Grass—Lightweight, fragrance free, biodegradable, clumps well, fine particles, but tracks easily.
- ☻ Upcycled coffee grounds—good odor control, clumps well, may be mixed with other ingredients such as cornstarch which can be allergenic. Tracks easily. Cats may not like the smell.

If your cat is avoiding the litter box, you may need to place different types of litter in boxes side-by-side. Let your cat show you what he prefers.

Types of litter cats prefer:

1. Smaller litter particles
2. Odor-free

Types of litter owners prefer:

1. Clumping
2. Odor absorbent
3. Low dust
4. Low tracking

You and your cat will have to find the best option that makes you both happy.

Pet-Proof Your Home

In addition to crate training, it is always a good idea to pet-proof areas your pet will be allowed to roam free within your home. Decide which areas the pet will be allowed to access. Gates can be used to block areas that are off limits until the pet is trained to remain in one area if that is your desire. Stairs, electric cords, children's toys, remote control batteries, toxic plants, medications, chemicals, and trash cans are dangers to consider within your home. I have even treated kittens and puppies that became trapped inside recliners and dryers. Tips to keep your pet safe include:

- Childproof latches to keep little paws from prying open cabinets. My cats excel at opening doors on closets and cabinets.
- Install window blinds without cords to prevent pets from getting tangled, ingesting cords, or choking.

- Place medications, cleaners, chemicals, and laundry supplies on high shelves or in locked cabinets.
- Keep trash cans covered or inside a latched cabinet.
- Make sure your kitten or cat has not jumped into the dryer before you turn it on.
- Keep harmful foods out of reach. Many food and candy products contain harmful ingredients such as xylitol, which can cause hypoglycemia and liver failure.
- Keep the toilet lid closed to prevent drowning or drinking of harmful cleaning chemicals.
- Place dangling wires from lamps, telephones, and other electronics out of reach.
- Put away children's toys and games. Small pieces are choking hazards and may cause intestinal obstruction if swallowed.
- Put knick-knacks on sturdy, high shelves where they cannot be broken or fall on your pet.
- Make sure all heating and air vents have covers.
- Put away all sewing and craft notions, especially thread and needles.
- Clean all antifreeze from the garage floor and driveway, as one taste can be lethal to animals.
- Keep all sharp objects and tools out of reach.
- Keep laundry and shoes behind closed doors (drawstrings, buttons, and shoelaces can cause major problems if swallowed).
- Keep any medications, lotions, and cosmetics off accessible surfaces (like the bedside table).
- Make sure swimming pools and ponds are not accessible to pets, as drowning and hypothermia can occur if they fall in and cannot find stairs to climb out.
- Lawn and garden chemicals and fertilizers should be stowed out of reach on shelves in the garage or garden shed.

- Move common house plants that may be poisonous out of reach, including hanging plants that can be jumped onto from nearby surfaces. Research plants in your yard that may be toxic if eaten.
- Do not put out rat or mouse poison in areas your pet can reach. This includes the basement and garage, as well as in cabinets inside the home.

Indoor and Outdoor Plants that are Toxic to Pets

- Amaryllis—It is toxic to both dogs and cats and can cause tremors, excessive drooling, breathing difficulties, and abdominal problems including diarrhea and vomiting.
- Autumn Crocus—There are two types of Crocus plants: one that blooms in the spring (Crocus species) and the other in the autumn (Colchicum Autumnale). The spring plants are more common and are part of the Iridaceae family. These ingestions can cause general gastrointestinal upset including vomiting and diarrhea. These should not be mistaken for Autumn Crocus, part of the Liliaceae family, which contain colchicine. The Autumn Crocus is highly toxic and can cause severe vomiting, gastrointestinal bleeding, liver and kidney damage, and respiratory failure.
- Azalea and Rhododendron—Avoid bringing a bunch of these beautiful flowers inside your home. Eating just a few leaves could cause vomiting and diarrhea.
- Castor Bean—The poisonous principle is ricin, a highly toxic protein that can produce severe abdominal pain, drooling, vomiting, diarrhea, excessive thirst, weakness, and loss of appetite. Severe cases can result in dehydration, muscle twitching, tremors, seizures, coma, and death.
- Cyclamen—These contain cyclamine, with the highest

concentration found in the root of the plant. Ingestion can result in significant gastrointestinal irritation, intense vomiting, dehydration, and death.

- Daffodil—If any part of this plant is ingested by your pet they may experience diarrhea, vomiting, abdominal pain, breathing problems, and/or heart arrhythmia. These flowers contain lycorine, an alkaloid with strong emetic properties (something that triggers vomiting). Crystals are found in the outer layer of the bulbs like hyacinths, which cause severe tissue irritation and secondary drooling. Daffodil ingestions can result in more severe symptoms so if an exposure is witnessed or symptoms are seen, I recommend seeking veterinary advice for further supportive care.

- Dieffenbachia—You might know this plant as Dumb Cane or Leopard Lily. Dieffenbachia can cause intense oral irritation, drooling, nausea, vomiting, and difficulty swallowing if ingested.

- Foxglove—This plant is poisonous to both pets and people. Even just a little bit of foxglove can kill a cat. The cardiac glycosides in foxglove can cause vomiting, diarrhea, muscle weakness, and heart failure. Even the water from a vase of cut foxglove flowers will be poisonous to pets, so keep it well protected, even inside.

- Hyacinth and Tulips—The bulbs are poisonous. If your dog is a digger, steer clear of these and other early bloomers such as snowdrops, crocuses, or daffodils. The toxic principle of these plants is very concentrated in the bulbs (versus the leaf or flower). When the plant parts or bulbs are chewed or ingested, it can result in tissue irritation to the mouth and esophagus. Typical signs include profuse drooling, vomiting, or even diarrhea, depending on the amount consumed. There is no specific antidote, but with supportive care, animals can do well. With large ingestions of the bulb, more severe symptoms such as an increase in heart rate and changes in respiration can occur.

- Iris—Part of the Iridaceae family, Iris is poisonous to both cats and dogs. The bulbs are the most toxic, so dogs prone to digging may be the most at risk. Ingestion can cause irritation to the gastrointestinal tract, resulting in vomiting, diarrhea, stomach pain, and drooling.

- Lilies (all Lilium species, such as Easter Lilies)—There are dangerous and benign lilies. Peace, Peruvian, and Calla lilies contain oxalate crystals that cause minor signs, such as tissue irritation to the mouth, tongue, pharynx, and esophagus; this results in minor drooling. The more dangerous, potentially fatal lilies are true lilies, including Tiger, Day, Asiatic, Easter, and Japanese Show lilies, all of which are highly toxic to cats. Even small ingestions (such as two or three petals or leaves) can result in severe kidney failure. If your cat is seen consuming any part of a lily, take your cat and the plant immediately to a veterinarian for medical care.

- Lily of the Valley—This plant contains cardiac glycosides which can adversely affect your pet's heart rate or cause severe arrhythmias or seizures. This is in addition to gastrointestinal issues such as vomiting and diarrhea.

- Morning Glory—The seeds of some species of Morning Glory contain lysergic acid, which is essentially a natural form of LSD. It can cause hallucinations, disorientation, tremors, and gastrointestinal problems in both dogs and cats. Avoid planting this vining plant. If it is already growing, make sure the seed-containing flowers are not eaten.

- Oleander—This is an outdoor evergreen that thrives in warm climates. It produces flowers in many colors. The flowers and leaves are poisonous to pets and humans. Ingestion causes severe vomiting, slowed heart rate, and possibly death.
- Sago Palm—All parts are poisonous, but the seed or "nuts" contain the largest amount of toxin. Ingestion of just one or two seeds can result in vomiting, diarrhea, depression, seizures, and liver failure.
- Schefflera—These contain oxalate crystals that can cause oral irritation, excessive drooling, vomiting, difficulty in swallowing, intense burning, and irritation of the mouth, lips, and tongue.
- Yew—Contains taxine, which causes central nervous system effects such as trembling, coordination problems, and difficulty breathing. It can also cause significant gastrointestinal irritation and cardiac failure, which can result in death.

Foods that may be Toxic to Pets

- Grapes and raisins—Not all pets are susceptible to illness caused by this fruit; unfortunately, there is no way to know if your pet will become sick. My son's Cocker spaniel found and ate a pound of grapes with no ill effects. I have treated other dogs that have gone into kidney failure after eating one or two grapes. Raisins are more toxic than grapes. It is best to avoid feeding them.
- Chocolate—Contains theobromine which can cause hyperactivity, seizures, tremors, irregular heartbeat, and death. Theobromine is much more concentrated in dark

chocolate than milk chocolate. Be sure to hide all candy, cake, and cookies containing chocolate out of reach from your pet.

- Macadamia nuts—May cause vomiting, weakness, tremors, drunken walk, and death.
- Apricot, Peach, Cherry, and Plum pits—Contain cyanide; causes vomiting, shock, cardiac arrest, and death. They are also the perfect size to cause intestinal obstruction.
- Onions and scallions—May cause hemolytic anemia, especially in cats, vomiting, diarrhea, and bloody urine. Effects of eating onions are cumulative. Garlic is in the same family of plants but is not as toxic in dogs. Garlic should not be routinely fed to cats or any dog with a history of anemia.
- Green tomatoes, tomato vines, and leaves—Can cause vomiting, diarrhea, and seizures.
- Raw and green potatoes—Can cause vomiting, diarrhea, seizures, and heart arrhythmias. Cooked potatoes are fine to feed.
- Rhubarb—Can cause kidney failure in dogs due to an antinutrient called oxalic acid which creates crystals in the urinary tract that can cause the kidneys to shut down. Signs of rhubarb poisoning can include drooling, vomiting, diarrhea, tremors, bloody urine, and changes in thirst.
- Nutmeg—Causes tremors, muscle spasms, seizures, and death.
- Persimmon seeds—cause vomiting, diarrhea, and fever.
- Raw Dough or Yeast—Produces ethanol, causing liver failure, seizures, drunken gait, coma, and death.
- Alcohol—Causes depression, weakness, liver failure, coma, and death.
- Raw Salmon or Trout—Can carry parasites that cause

Salmon Poisoning Disease. Canned, frozen, or cooked fish is okay. Fish should be frozen for a minimum of two weeks before feeding raw.

- Avocado peel—Causes vomiting, diarrhea, and edema (swelling with fluid). The meat of the avocado is fine however it is toxic for birds.
- Edible marijuana products—Cause panting, uncontrollable thirst, drooling, slow responses, dribbling urine, increased heart rate, hyperactivity, coma, seizures, and death due to the THC in the product.
- Acorns—May cause vomiting, diarrhea, kidney disease, and intestinal obstruction.
- Bleu Cheese—Contains roquefortine C, which is toxic, particularly for dogs. Vomiting, diarrhea, twitching, seizures, and high body temperature may be the result.
- Corn cobs—Ingestion may result in intestinal obstruction. Do not give these to your pet!
- Any food containing xylitol—Candy, gum, peanut butter, toothpaste, baked goods, but can be found in many foods as an artificial sweetening ingredient. Low blood sugar and liver failure can occur when even small amounts are ingested.
- Tobacco, including cigarettes, e-cigarettes, liquid nicotine, chewing tobacco, nicotine inhalers, and cigars—Can cause vomiting, abnormal heart rate, tremors, and weakness, usually within one hour of ingestion.

Dangerous Toys, Treats, and Household Items

- Rawhides—These are chemically treated leather products that are not digestible, which makes them a choking and obstruction hazard. They are commonly contaminated with bacteria. They can contain formaldehyde, ethoxyquin, arsenic or other potentially harmful compounds. BHA (butylated hydroxyanisole) and BHT (butylated hydroxy-toluene) are preservatives that are commonly used in the creation of rawhide; they are known cancer-causing agents.

- Children's toys—Stuffed animals are fun to shred but can cause constipation or obstruction when eaten. Small toys are choking and obstruction hazards.
- Coins—These can cause obstruction. Coins containing zinc can cause anemia and death; pennies are mostly zinc.
- Baby bottle nipples and pacifiers—They taste good, particularly if they are used. They are the perfect size to cause bowel obstruction.
- Diapers, wipes, and tissues—Be sure to dispose of these in covered trash cans as they commonly cause obstructions resulting in surgical removal when eaten.
- Balls, particularly small balls—They can become lodged in the airway or in the intestines. A ball should always be too large to swallow. Golf balls are problematic and should never be used as a pet toy. Tennis balls are not meant to be used as chew toys; they come apart easily and the fuzzy outer covering is abrasive to teeth and the digestive tract. I once had to remove tennis ball fuzz causing an obstruction in the stomach of a nine-week-old puppy.
- Vinyl toys containing phthalates—A reputable company will state that vinyl toys are BPA (bisphenol A) and phthalate -free. BPA and phthalates are used in plastics; they have been associated with infertility, cancer, and endocrine disorders.
- Pig ears and cow hooves—These products are often

included in recalls for contamination with Salmonella and E. coli bacteria. Pig ears can get lodged in a dog's throat and cause them to choke. If chewed the wrong way, they can also get very sharp and rip a dog's esophagus or stomach lining when swallowed. Cow hooves have been shown to crack and fracture teeth.

- Hard antlers—If your dog is an aggressive chewer these can fracture or erode teeth.
- Ropes or string toys—Toys with long pieces of rope or string can cause intestinal blockages or tear the intestines which can result in death. I once lost a Doberman patient because the owner made a ball of string for the dog to play with. He unraveled it and swallowed enough string to rip his intestines to shreds.
- Squeaky toys—If your dog loves to pull out the squeakers, be sure they are not swallowing them. These are a choking and obstruction hazard.
- Plastic bags—Cats and puppies love pouncing on plastic bags. However, they can get heads or limbs entangled in bag handles or get their head into the bag, which can result in suffocation.
- Rubber bands—I have treated many dogs and cats over the years with rubber bands placed on their ears and legs. Children playing groomer with their pets may place these around limbs, cutting off circulation. In long-haired cats and dogs, they may not be found until the limb or ear is swollen, which may require surgical repair or even amputation. Teach your children never to use rubber bands on pets.
- Prescription and non-prescription medications—One acetaminophen tablet can kill a cat. Ibuprofen, naproxen, and other over-the-counter pain medications can be

equally harmful for cats and dogs. Keep all medications out of reach and securely stored. Never give medications to your pet without seeking veterinary advice.

Taking the time to pet-proof your home and yard can save money on medical emergencies and possibly save a life. The old saying "An ounce of prevention is worth a pound of cure" is true.

10

Environmental Enrichment

While dogs may have the opportunity to play in the yard, go for walks, or play with neighborhood friends, they still spend most of their time within the home. It is important to provide environmental enrichment inside the home for your pet if it has limited outdoor time. Enrichment activities can also help slow cognitive decline and provide physical stimulation for senior pets.

The Ohio State University College of Veterinary Medicine instituted the Indoor Pet Initiative to address behavioral enrichment. They define this as "the process of manipulating an animal's environment to increase physical activity and normal species typical behavior that satisfies the animal's physical and psychological needs. It reduces stress and therefore promotes overall health by increasing an animal's perception of control over their environment and by occupying their time."

They identified five categories that may be used:

1. Food-based enrichment
2. Sensory enrichment (sight, smell, touch, hear, taste)
3. Novel objects
4. Social enrichment
5. Positive training

By mimicking behaviors pets might engage in the wild, indoor pets can stalk, hunt, and catch small "prey" items while climbing, running, and resting throughout the day. Treat balls with small bits of food can be pushed and chased, with the treats as the "reward" for catching the prey. Hiding treats around the room, encouraging your dog or cat to find the hidden treasures, keeps them moving while rewarding them for searching.

Some cats become bored and stressed because they do not have the thrill of the hunt to procure food. You can help these cats by providing games or toys that they roll or bat to get food to be released. There are a lot of toys made for dogs for this purpose which would work just as well for cats. Wet food can be placed in a jar lying on its side, so the cat must reach in to pull the food out. It can also be mashed into the bottom of muffin tins or in slow-feeder bowls that make the cat work to get all the food. This type of feeding may work better for single cat households or in small groups where the cats get along well.

Feeding on platters such as the Mine Pet Platter provides instinctive, healthier eating behaviors and engages the minds of cats and dogs using indentations, crevices, and curves that encourage licking, tracking, foraging, and other natural stimulating feeding behaviors.

Even though dogs have more opportunities to spend time on leash walks or playing in the yard, they still enjoy the ability to watch what is going on outside. Perches or furniture placed by windows allow indoor animals to watch wildlife and outdoor activities throughout the day. Many dogs and cats love to lie on the top of the sofa or chair placed nearest to a large window. Cats, and some dogs, adore climbing into and playing with cardboard boxes and paper bags. During inclement weather try setting up mazes or obstacle courses for your pet to navigate.

Laser lights are great for increasing exercise and getting a pet moving. Both our dogs and cats will chase a laser light. Chasing can be very frustrating if the pet never gets to "catch" the light (prey). Be sure to offer a treat or reward when they finish the game.

Puzzle toys are another great way to entertain house-bound pets. Puzzle toys are used as a means of combining the natural reward of feeding with physical and mental stimulation. Small, high-value treats are hidden behind sliding doors or under removable puzzle pieces that can be nudged with nose or paws. Cats enjoy these as much as dogs. The use of puzzle toys should be monitored the first time a new toy is introduced to ensure that the toy is not being destroyed and consumed. The use of puzzle toys in a household with multiple pets should also be closely monitored to ensure the pets do not guard these toys from one another.

Cats generally do not have the opportunity to roam outside; I have only seen a few that walk on leashes with harnesses. Some pet owners use a stroller or a catio, which is an outdoor enclosure that allows cats to safely experience the great outdoors. A traditional style catio is attached to the home, offering an easy way to get in and out of the cat sanctuary. The catio is enclosed with chicken coup wire (or another material similar in nature) that provides ventilation but keeps the kitty inside where it is safer and secure. Catios can be filled with furniture, scratching posts, toys, and hammocks to lounge around and exercise. If the catio is going to be exposed to direct sunlight in certain spots, having furniture that is designed for protection against sun will be important. Portable catios that look like mesh tunnels are available if you cannot build a permanent catio onto your home.

Cats can learn to walk on a harness and leash, although few cat owners consider this option. If your pet is a kitten, it is best to introduce this activity early, once the kitten is comfortable in his new home. Start by letting the cat wander around the house wearing a well-fitted harness when you are home. Once the cat tolerates the harness, attach a leash to the harness and walk around the house. Treats may be used as bribes to get the cat moving in a forward direction. If all goes well, you will be able to start taking kitty outside for tours around your yard. It is recommended to stay close to home in a quiet area when first starting. If the cat has been kept indoors for most of its life, the outside world can be a very scary place. Noises and movement can startle the cat; be prepared for the cat to bolt by keeping a firm grip on the leash. Once your cat calmly walks on the harness and leash, you can go on bigger adventures.

Cats are often thought of as low-maintenance pets, and while they are usually far more independent than their canine counterparts, they can be prone to developing behavioral problems if they become bored or frustrated. Problems can include aggression, over-grooming, hair pulling, and overeating.

Psychological stress in multi-cat households can be a problem. Cats need space of their own, a place to hide and rest without the bother of housemate interaction. They need a safe haven where they can hide from intruders; each cat in the house will determine a place that is considered their own territory. When cats do not have the ability to get away from others, they can start to show unwanted behaviors. They may lash out at other animals or people in the household. Some cats have been known to become aggressive, hiding and waiting to pounce on the unsuspecting intruder that might enter their territory. They draw an invisible line that must not be crossed; most cats in the house understand the boundaries set by others. Problems can arise when a new cat is introduced into the household, especially if the newcomer challenges the territory of the resident cats.

When a cat or dog dies or is removed from the household, there will also be a shifting of territories and pecking order among the remaining cats and dogs, particularly if the pet that is no longer present was higher up in the group ranking. Be vigilant for behavior changes during these stressful times.

In addition to hiding places, cats need vertical spaces for climbing and safety. The cats that are higher in the hierarchy tend to claim the highest perch, but lower ranking members may prefer higher perches so they can visually keep track of bullies and aggressors. Cats may vie for space if only a few high perches are available. Providing cat trees, shelves, or window perches can alleviate battles over vertical territory.

Cats have natural instincts to scratch. Encourage them by providing scratching posts, cat trees, or boxes for them to scratch. Each cat has a preferred surface. If your cat is destroying your furniture or woodwork, try different types of scratching posts with carpet, rope, or corrugated cardboard.

By providing environmental stimulation, you can keep your pet active and mentally and physically stimulated, which should result in less behavioral problems. The number one reason pets are turned into shelters is bad behavior, which can be avoided by providing a loving home that provides social interaction and environmental stimulation, along with good training.

11

Finding a Trainer

Not everyone needs a trainer for their new addition to the household, but good behavior is not an automatic given. Depending on whether you welcome a new puppy or kitten or an older pet into your home, bad behaviors may already be ingrained. Training can be a great way to teach everything from basic commands, to how to interact with other animals or people. The time spent on training sessions is great bonding time as well as serving as a form of environmental enrichment.

If you have worked with animals in the past, you may have a good idea how to train your new pet. Cats need to learn manners, just as dogs need to be well-behaved. Most people do not want cats walking on kitchen tables and counters or being destructive to furnishings. If you are having trouble with teaching your pet specific behaviors, you may need to commit to working with a trainer. It is important to make sure the trainer you choose is the right fit for you and your pet. Look for a trainer who uses positive reinforcement to train, not punishment. Ask for referrals from other pet owners.

Pet training is an unregulated industry, meaning there are no national, state, or local licenses required. Anyone can call themselves a trainer, so it is important to research the background on anyone you are considering hiring. Just like humans, not all dogs or cats are the same; they may learn and respond differently in any given situation. Some animals learn best when trained in one-on-one sessions, while others need to learn in a group setting where there are distractions.

Training of the pet parent is just as important as training the pet. It is up to you to determine whether the pet will be allowed on the furniture or to eat from the table at mealtime. Pets need a consistent set of rules; they will not understand if the rules change depending on your mood. If hiring a trainer, they need to be able to teach you as well as the pet.

While no formal training is required for someone to say they are a trainer, the Certification Council for Professional Dog Trainers does offer certifications based on experience and testing.

The designations are: CPDT-KA®, CPDT-KSA®, CBCC-KA®.

CPDT-KA® indicates that a dog trainer has passed a comprehensive exam and has at least 300 hours of dog training experience.

CPDT-KSA® indicates that a dog trainer has passed a comprehensive exam *and* an objective skills-based assessment along with at least 300 hours of dog training experience.

CBCC-KA® indicates that a dog behavior consultant has passed a comprehensive exam on behavior modification and has at least 300 hours of dog behavior consulting experience.

Not all dog trainers have experience dealing with cats. The Animal Behavior College offers a course to become a certified cat trainer. Finding someone who has completed the course might be a good place to start if you need help with kitty issues.

For more complicated behavior issues, most veterinary colleges have trained veterinary behaviorists that can be very helpful and a good resource.

If you need to hire a trainer or behavior counselor, the following should be taken into consideration:

- What are the specific concerns that need to be addressed?
- Are these basic training issues, or behavioral concerns?
- Are you looking for private training, a group class, or a board-and-train facility?
- How involved do family members need or want to be? Is the behavior problem directed toward certain members of the household?
- What are you willing and able to pay? Be realistic in your expectations.
- How much time and effort can you reasonably devote to working with your pet?
- Does the trainer have specific experience with the age and breed of your pet?
- If you need a trainer for a cat behavioral issue, does the trainer have experience with cats?

Questions you should ask the trainer:

- Why did you get into training and why do you do this work?
- What experience do you have with this breed?
- What experience do you have dealing with the particular issues I am having?

- What formal training do you have?
- Do you belong to any professional associations?
- What styles of training do you use?
- What type of contract do you require?
- What is the fee? Is that per session or a set number of sessions? Training can be expensive, particularly if you opt for in-home visits or individual sessions. If the fees are more than you are prepared to spend, consider looking for online or group classes.
- Ask for references. Check out online reviews.

12

Basic Training

Heather Szasz, owner of Happy Owner Happy Dog, was kind enough to submit some training tips. She is committed to enabling pet owners to have the ultimate relationship with their pets. She is an Animal Behavior College mentor who states that a positive owner makes a happy dog; a well-behaved dog makes a happy owner.

LEASH TRAINING

There are many harnesses, collars, and leashes on the market, making it hard to determine which works best for your dog. Puppies should be in a harness so that the neck will not be damaged if they pull with the leash attached to the collar. Also, with older dogs that you may adopt into your family, I prefer a no-pull harness that hooks at the front and the back with a double leash. Having two points of contact allows the handler to increase and decrease control, as needed. The leash is just as important as the harness. It must be a regular 4- or 6-foot leash, not a retractable leash. Retractable leashes are dangerous, harming many animals and their handlers. Cats can also be fitted with harnesses if you want to train them to walk on a leash.

First, your pet needs to get used to the harness and leash in the house before training to walk outside. You want to pair fun activities with wearing them. Feed your pet, play with your pet, call your pet to you, all with the harness and leash on; reward with food or treats when they come to you. Remember, training is for short amounts of time. You will need plenty of patience for this training.

Leash training should be practiced at home first. This is so much easier for your pet to stay focused on you since they are more used to their home environment rather than outside where there are lots of new sights, sounds, and smells! Stand next to your pet with the leash in a loose loop and give him several treats in a row for standing or sitting next to your leg.

1. Take one step forward and encourage him to follow by giving another treat as he catches up.

2. Continue giving treats to your pet at the level of your knee or hip as you walk forward.

3. When he runs in front of you, simply turn in the opposite direction, call him to you, and reward him in place. Then continue. Gradually begin giving treats further apart (from every step to every other step, every third step, and so on).

Remember, all training should be fun for you and your pet. When you learn something new, it takes time to master. Repetition is key.

Older dogs who have been adopted may have had no leash training or may have been allowed to pull on the leash. I would advise you to get a no-pull harness with the double leash. Begin the training as you would for puppy training. Because the dog is older, your treats need to be more desirable. I suggest you use these treats only for leash training. You can start this training in the backyard or in the driveway or drive to a quiet location, where you can focus on each other.

BASIC OBEDIENCE SKILLS

Dogs love to learn. Working breeds need to have a "job" that keeps them fulfilled and out of trouble. While many people think that cats are not trainable, cats are quite capable of learning the same commands as dogs.

Sit

The first skill to teach them is the "Sit" command. Once learned, this can be used for many reasons: teaching them to wait patiently for meals or treats, as a calming method when in a stressful situation, and as a method to encourage them to focus.

There are two different methods for showing your dog what "sit" means. The first method is called capturing. This is where we capture the sit when it naturally happens. When your puppy or dog sits you say "YES!" and reward them with food or treats. Then move away and see if your puppy comes to you; wait for the sit. Say "YES!" and reward again. Once he is consistent at giving you this position, now just before he sits, you can say "Sit".

The next option is called luring. Get down in front of your pet, holding a treat as a lure. Put the treat right in front of the pet's nose, then slowly lift the food above his head. He will probably sit as he lifts his head to nibble at the treat. Allow him to eat the treat when his bottom touches the ground. Practice a few times and again, when he is consistent with the position, say "Sit" just before he sits. You can start to wean off the food or treats, using your hand motion without the treats to lure in place.

Never physically put your puppy or older dog into the sitting position; this can be confusing or upsetting to some dogs, especially if you have adopted a pet who may have a bad experience with humans pushing down the rear end or if there is any spinal or pelvic arthritis pain.

Touch

You can use hand targeting to keep your pet's focus. This can make veterinary or grooming visits go more smoothly by being able to direct your pet's head and body in a specific direction (instead of manhandling him into the perfect position). You can use it to help with loose leash walking (the dog cannot forge ahead if he is targeting his nose to your hand). This also helps with having the dog come to you. Cats can be taught to walk on leads also; start by following your cat where he wants to go, eventually teaching him to follow where you lead.

Start by rubbing a treat on one of your hands. Put your hand up to your pet's face and say "Touch". They will immediately touch as they are attracted to the scent. Offer praise and reward. Repeat each time with your hand close to your pet's face. Once he understands that "touch" means touch your hand, you can start to create distance from your pet's face. Make sure you do not go too far away from his face, because the training should be fun without you saying no because he did not touch your hand.

Come

This is one of the most important skills you can teach your pet. Whether they escape out of the door, or the leash comes out of your hand when walking, recall is an essential safety skill. You need to make this a positive experience for them. Teaching them to respond to their name is the first step. When you adopt an older pet, they may have a new name if they were in the shelter. Call their name; when they look at you, reward them. Play hide and seek in the house and the yard by calling their name and waiting for them to find you, then reward them.

When you are teaching your pet to come, make sure you start in your home. Move a short distance from the pet, call his or her name to get his attention and then say come; start moving backwards encouraging the pet to come to you. As soon as he reaches you, praise him and offer a reward. You can also call your pet by name, bend down, and open your arms to encourage him to come to you. You need to make this so exciting that no matter what distractions are around, your pet is attracted to your excitement.

With older pets I would train the same as the youngsters. Remember they may have not been taught this skill or may have had bad experiences with previous owners who reprimanded them for not coming when called. Also, when training outside with more distractions, your treats must be high value, such as dehydrated meats, chicken, or turkey. The reward must match the level of training.

Prevent Destructive Behavior

Puppies and kittens are renowned for destructive behavior. We must understand that they learn the world through their mouth. Is it edible, how does it feel, does it taste good? Chewing can also help a pet de-stress.

With puppies it is better to avoid destructive behavior whenever possible, rather than trying to correct it after it has occurred. The rule of thumb when your puppy is 8 weeks old, until it is responsible for not doing this behavior is:

1. 100% supervision when out of the crate.

2. Give suitable chews for the puppy.

3. Do not give toys that are similar to your children's toys.

For older dogs, they may chew because they are bored, have anxiety, or suffer separation anxiety. Make sure you stimulate your dog with mental stimulation exercises; provide good quality exercise, walks, or playtime. If your dog is chewing because it is anxious or has separation anxiety, you may need to seek advice from your veterinarian or professional dog trainer for the best course of action.

How our energy impacts our pets

As pet owners we do not consider how our energy, emotions, and attitudes impact our pets. Our pets gravitate towards positive energy and walk away from negative energy. The pets in our lives are constantly giving us feedback about the energy levels we are putting off. You may notice that your puppy is acting just like your children. If your dog gets excited when a guest is at the door, is that because you are excited? If your pet does not seem to trust people, is that because you do not trust people? If your pet is afraid of fireworks or thunderstorms, are you? If your pet does not like children, do you?

Are you comparing this dog or cat to the last dog or cat you had? Your pet knows this and will not be as bonded to you as you think they are. Are you still grieving your last pet while you have the new puppy or kitten in your house?

Our emotions are not hidden from our pets. They know what is going on with us all the time. We cannot lie to them; they know the truth.

If your pet is anxious, perhaps you are anxious or worrying, with your mind going a mile a minute, overthinking minor events.

When your pet is giving you a particular behavior, take the time to check in with yourself to see where your energy is, or your emotion, or your attitude. Take some deep breaths, re-focus and see how your pet responds. The results may surprise you!

For more information on how to balance your behavior with your pet's, please visit https://www.happyownerhappydog.com/

13

Grooming

Grooming needs will correspond with the type and breed of pet, but all pets will require basic grooming care. You may be able to perform needed grooming at home or may need to call in a professional. Finding a reputable groomer is essential. Ask for references from neighbors and friends; your veterinarian may also have some suggestions. I recommend trying to find a mobile groomer that will come to your home or a groomer that only has a few pets present at one time rather than having your pet exposed to large numbers of animals or having to sit all day in a cage waiting to be groomed. Many pets have died at grooming facilities when left unattended in drying cages or tubs.

Regular grooming should include inspection of the body from nose to tail. Look for any cuts, lumps, or skin discoloration that may require veterinary attention. The coat should be kept clean and free from mats. Ears should be free from discharge and nails need to be kept trimmed, generally needing to be trimmed every four to six weeks.

A healthy coat will be soft and relatively smooth even on short- or wire-haired breeds. The coat should be shiny, but not greasy and should not have a strong odor. A pet with an unhealthy coat may have dry, brittle hair with a lot of loose hair or flakes in the coat, greasy clumping coat, or patches of missing hair.

Regular brushing is one of the most important aspects of grooming. Brushing pulls the natural oils through the coat from the skin and removes loose hair. Long-coated dogs and cats may need daily brushing to prevent mats from forming while short-coated animals may maintain a healthy coat with weekly brushing. Combs or brushes with rotating teeth work well to remove minor tangles. Brush before bathing to remove mats, as mats will be harder to brush out once they get wet. Never use scissors to cut out mats. Many animals suffer injuries when owners try to cut tangled hair away from the body. If the pet is so matted that brushing will not remove the mats, please take them to your groomer or veterinarian for professional care.

Most pets do not need to be bathed often, unless they spend a lot of time outside in mud and dirt. Bathing more than weekly may result in a dry coat. Essential oil shampoos or soaps that do not have chemical detergents are best. Human shampoos should not be used on animals, as they tend to be too drying. Using a good conditioner or moisturizer formulated for pets is a good idea after bathing.

Ears should be clean and free of debris, odor, and redness. If water gets in the ears while bathing, a drying agent should be used to remove it. Witch hazel works well. Place a dropper of witch hazel in the ear canal, massage the base of the ear, and wipe any liquid away with a cotton ball. Do not use cotton swabs in the ear canals, as you may damage the sensitive tissue lining the ears. If there is excessive discharge, odor, or redness, make an appointment with your veterinarian.

Pay particular attention to wrinkles and facial folds, particularly in short-nosed pets. Some short-tailed breeds will also have pockets or folds near the tail. These folds commonly harbor bacterial infections because they are hot and moist. Check the folds and clean daily if needed.

Trimming nails can be difficult for many pet owners. If your pet will not allow you to trim the nails or you do not feel comfortable trimming them at home, the pet should have professional trims every four to six weeks. Some pets are more tolerant of the nail Dremel rather than the clippers. Nail clippers should be sharp, as dull clippers can cause pain.

Teaching your pet to allow you to handle his feet will go a long way toward getting nails trimmed hassle-free. Try having someone distract your pet with food or belly rubs while you trim the nails.

Styptic powder can be used to stop bleeding if you happen to cut a nail too short (your pet will only let this happen once or twice before deciding they hate nail trimming). Regular baking flour can also be used to stop bleeding.

If you want to clip your dog or cat's hair at home, be sure to invest in high-quality clippers with a number 10 blade attachment. Place the animal on a table that is a comfortable height for you to reach, making sure the animal feels secure. Have someone hold your pet while you clip. Be very careful around the face, ears, and anal regions—do not attempt to clip if your pet is moving around. Hair should be shaved when the coat is clean and dry, not wet.

Be sure your clipper blades are clean and sharp. Start around the pet's neck, working your way down the body, keeping the blade flat against the skin. Be careful around thin skin, the underarms, and flanks. Check the blades often to make sure they are not getting too hot, as they can burn the skin. If you feel unsure about shaving your pet at home, consider leaving this step in the grooming process to the experts or enroll in classes to learn how to safely groom your pet at home.

14

Tummy Trouble on Arrival

In general, it is recommended to continue feeding the same diet the pet has been eating for at least the first few weeks in the new home. However, I have strong feelings about differences in quality of pet foods on the market and I admit it would be difficult for me to continue feeding a low-quality food to a new pet entering my home. I will go into this in more depth in later chapters; for now, suffice it to say I have no dry kibble in my home and would be extremely reluctant to allow it to cross my threshold.

Transitioning to a new home and family can result in gastrointestinal upset due to immune system stress. Quick changes in diet may contribute to further tummy trouble, so patience in changing to the diet you prefer is generally advised. Probiotics can help ease the diet transition and boost the immune system. I recommend starting a high-quality probiotic immediately.

Please avoid probiotics containing Animal Digest. The most popular product sold by traditional veterinarians contains this ingredient as a flavor enhancer. Unfortunately, this ingredient has a good chance of being contaminated with euthanasia solution, as stated by the Food and Drug Administration: "There appear to be associations between rendered or hydrolyzed ingredients and the presence of pentobarbital in dog food. The ingredients Meat and Bone Meal, Beef and Bone Meal, Animal Fat, and Animal Digest are rendered or hydrolyzed from animal sources that could include euthanized animals." The FDA has been aware that pet food is commonly contaminated with euthanasia solution since the mid-1990's. To date, they have chosen not to enforce laws against the use of euthanized animals in pet food.

Other supplements that may help the transition include products that contain slippery elm, montmorillonite or bentonite clay, pumpkin fiber, ginger, L-glutamine, or digestive enzymes. Many of these are available on my website www.drjudymorgan.com. Sometimes a simple spoonful of canned pumpkin added to a few meals can help dramatically.

A stool sample should be taken to your veterinarian as soon as possible. If you already have pets in your home, adding an infected individual to the group can result in the spread of parasites through all animals in the household. Until you have determined the new pet is parasite-free or has been treated for parasites, it is important to use one area of the yard for the new pet to use for potty breaks. Clean up stool immediately to prevent other pets from being exposed.

Testing for intestinal parasites should be performed, rather than just automatically giving a generic de-wormer. There are many de-worming medications available; different products treat different parasites. The only way to know which to choose, if any, is by testing a fecal sample. Testing is only about eighty percent accurate, so it is advised to have a second sample tested in a week or two if the first one is negative. If the first test is positive, a second stool sample should be tested after de-worming is completed to make sure all parasites were cleared.

If the pet has diarrhea, feeding a bland diet can help calm the gastrointestinal tract. The following recipes can be used for dogs or cats.

MY BLAND DIET RECIPE

- ☐ 1 pound ground or chopped low-fat turkey, pork, or rabbit, baked, boiled, or sautéed

- ☐ 1 teaspoon grated fresh ginger root

- ☐ 12 ounces well-cooked mashed apple or pumpkin

- ☐ 4 ounces Portobello mushroom chopped and sautéed in olive or coconut oil (these can be left out if you cannot find them or do not have them on hand; white or Shiitake mushrooms will also work)

Mix all ingredients. Feed small quantities multiple times per day until normal stool is observed. Feed warm, not cold from the refrigerator. The pet will need approximately one cup of food for every fifteen to twenty pounds of adult body weight per day.

This recipe can be used until the stool has become firm. If stool does not return to normal within a few days or if there is blood in the stool, seek veterinary help.

To save time and effort, all raw ingredients may be placed in a slow cooker and cooked on low for six to eight hours.

Another option is congee. Served warm, most pets find it comforting and will eat it readily. I recommend making congee and freezing small batches for use as needed since it takes quite a while to make.

CONGEE RECIPE

- ☐ 1 cup long grain white rice (easier to digest than brown, lower fiber, higher starch)
- ☐ 1 cup diced boneless, skinless chicken breast (substitute pork tenderloin or rabbit if pet does not do well with chicken)
- ☐ ¼ cup grated fresh ginger root
- ☐ 8 cups water

Place all ingredients in a soup pot on the stove or a slow cooker. Simmer on low on the stove for 8 to 12 hours, stirring occasionally and adding water as needed. Or cook in a slow cooker on low for 24 hours, stirring occasionally. The longer it cooks, the more nutritious it will be. When finished, the rice and meat should be fully disintegrated, leaving a nice gruel. Congee is very easily digested and strengthens the digestive function.

Once your pet has formed stools, gradually reintroduce their regular diet over a period of a few days.

15

Vaccines

Depending on where the pet was obtained, vaccinations may have been given prior to purchase or adoption. Many dogs and cats are already over-vaccinated prior to arriving at your home. Vaccinations have been a wonderful addition to the health of animals and people everywhere; however, the overuse and misuse of vaccinations has also become a problem.

My thoughts on vaccinations have changed greatly over the years. When I was in veterinary school in the early 1980's, parvovirus in dogs was just being recognized. Thousands of dogs died from this horrific gastrointestinal disease prior to the invention of the parvovirus vaccine. I am not against vaccinations, but I strongly believe we must vaccinate responsibly to avoid over-stimulation of the immune system and resultant autoimmune diseases.

Typically, dogs and cats are vaccinated against rabies when they are four to six months old, then again one year later and every three years after that. Beginning in 1987, the state of Pennsylvania required cats to be vaccinated annually for rabies. Rabies is transmitted through bite wounds from infected animals. Since this is a zoonotic disease (can be spread from animals to people) with no treatment once infected, it was important to vaccinate as many pets as possible to stop the transmission of disease from wildlife. The biggest flaw with the system was that stray cats and barn cats were the animals that needed protection and they were not the animals being vaccinated. House cats that were being presented annually to the veterinarian were being over-immunized.

In 1985, the first Feline Leukemia vaccine became available for use and many veterinarians recommended vaccinating every cat. Feline Leukemia is a virus that is transmitted from one infected cat to another through bodily secretions and there is no effective treatment for the disease, once infected. Again, the wrong cats were being immunized. Feral, stray, and barn cats that should have been immunized were rarely caught and taken to the veterinarian, but house cats were being immunized for a disease for which they would have no exposure.

Suddenly, in the early 1990's, the University of Pennsylvania and the University of California at Davis veterinary pathology laboratories had more tissue samples than ever before from tumors in cats. Through years of research, it was determined that cats were making sarcoma tumors related to products in vaccines. Rabies and Feline Leukemia vaccines were incriminated. Heavy metals and preservatives in the vaccines acted as foreign material within the body. The immune system of the cats tried to wall off the offending foreign material and extrude it from the body, leaving large open cancerous wounds that were impossible to heal. Most of the tumors were located between the shoulder blades on the backs of cats, as that was the most common site used for injection of vaccines.

Since the discovery of the vaccine-related sarcoma problem recommendations have been made to give the rabies vaccination as low as possible on the right hind leg and the Feline Leukemia vaccination as low as possible on the left hind leg. The reasoning is that if a vaccine-related sarcoma occurs, the leg can be amputated. Personally, I find it offensive that instead of limiting vaccinations or changing to thimerosal-free (the mercury-based preservative) vaccines, we instead choose to remove body parts.

Fast forward a decade. More owners started keeping cats inside, often declawing them (which is now being banned in many areas), eliminating any outdoor time and exposure to viruses. Pets were being treated more like family members and children, not being allowed to roam the countryside. Yet, these cats and dogs were still being vaccinated annually for diseases to which they had no exposure. This, I consider, is misuse of vaccines.

For years, dogs and cats have been bombarded with anywhere from five to ten disease antigens in one vaccination visit and this has been repeated annually. Slowly we have begun to see more cases of hypothyroidism, hyperthyroidism, tumors, adrenal gland disease (Cushing's and Addison's), immune-mediated diseases, cancers, allergies, and long-term inflammatory illnesses. Researchers are starting to link overuse of vaccinations to these diseases.

Pet vaccination strategies are constantly changing; there is controversy over the ideal protocol. I feel that, unfortunately, most puppies and kittens receive many more vaccinations in their early life stages than are needed. Dogs and cats purchased from pet stores are commonly jabbed every week or two, with multi-valent (multiple disease) vaccines that just keep challenging the imma-ture immune system. This sets those animals up for a lifetime of immune system problems, including allergies, leaky gut, chronic infections, and inflammation.

Maternal immunity is passed from the mother to the newborns

through colostrum, which is the first milk on which they feed. The colostrum contains a lot of antibodies, which are large molecules that are easily absorbed in the newborns' gut during the first 24 hours of life. If the puppy or kitten misses out on the colostrum during the first 24 hours, they will not be able to absorb the antibodies later and will be left un-protected from disease.

The maternal immunity will protect the newborn during the first few weeks of life. The immunity derived in this manner will start to decline with time, usually reaching a low point between twelve and sixteen weeks of age. Vaccinations given when the maternal antibody is high will not produce immunization of the puppy or kitten; they will only serve to "poke" an immature immune system. One study showed that only 60% of puppies were able to respond to a vaccination at 16 weeks, but 95% could be immunized at 18 weeks.

A little immunology: Vaccines are made from modified variations of the virus, bacteria, or spirochete for the disease they are meant to protect against. Injecting a vaccination does not result in instant immunity. The body recognizes the organism in the vaccine as a foreign invader. The term for the invader is an *antigen*. In response to the antigen, the body makes a neutralizing agent called an *antibody*. The two fit together like puzzle pieces.

ANTIBODY

ANTIGEN

ANTIGEN-ANTIBODY COMPLEX

This response from the immune system, generated by the white blood cells known as lymphocytes, takes several days to build to maximum intensity, and the antibody concentration in the blood peaks at about 14 days. Giving serial vaccinations closer than 14 days apart is pointless, yet some breeders and pet stores vaccinate puppies and kittens weekly.

Sometimes the vaccination history of the pet is unknown, particularly if the pet was found as a stray. Most veterinarians will recommend starting the pet on a series of vaccinations as if they have never received a vaccine. This is an incorrect assumption. Most stray or adult animals will have developed some natural immunity to most of the common infections found in dogs and cats and may have received some prior vaccinations. The best way to determine whether vaccination is needed is by performing a titer. A titer can also be used to determine how well an animal has responded to vaccination.

A titer is a blood test that determines whether antibodies to certain organisms are present in the body. For dogs, distemper, hepatitis, and parvovirus titers are readily available through many reputable laboratories and there are in-house test kits (VacciCheck) that veterinarians can use. For cats, panleukopenia (distemper) titers are easily obtained. Rabies titers are available for both dogs and cats. The biggest drawback to performing titers is price. Some veterinarians do not want to be bothered with drawing blood for titers or do not understand their validity. In response, they quote exorbitant fees that many pet owners are unwilling or unable to afford. If this is the case, you can ask to have the blood drawn and sent to www.hemopet.org, Kansas State University Veterinary Diagnostic Laboratory, https://healthydogworkshop.com/titer-testing/ or www.protectthepets.com . These options are much more reasonably priced, generally.

Vaccine titers may last a lifetime or may wane over time. It is impossible to know exactly when antibody levels will drop. If you must show proof of protection for boarding, daycare, grooming, or frequent travel, annual titers should be acceptable. Not all animal care facilities will accept titers in place of vaccination, so be sure to check with them before arrival.

While vaccine titers show circulating antibody levels which may drop with time, a low titer does not necessarily mean the pet is no longer protected. After an immune response, memory cells are produced. The memory cells lay dormant in the lymphatic system for many years. If they detect a pathogen with the specific antigen, they rapidly multiply and secrete antibodies. This means that secondary exposure to a pathogen produces a much more rapid secondary response. This is an important function in vaccinations. Unfortunately, there is no easy way to detect memory cell response with a blood test, which means our pets may be well-protected once they have a positive titer. This protection may be life-long, even when detectable antibody titers drop.

My current recommendation for a new puppy includes vaccination against distemper at 12 to 14 weeks of age and parvovirus at 16 weeks of age. These are single vaccines, not combination vaccines. Most veterinarians do not carry single-disease vaccines; they use combination vaccines. When multiple-disease vaccines are given, the immune system must work harder to put more puzzle pieces together.

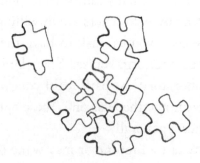

Following the two single vaccines I draw blood and perform a titer test at 20 weeks of age to determine whether the puppy has developed antibodies against the parvo and distemper viruses. Currently, my patients have about a 95% success rate for protection. Keep in mind that these puppies are not protected until they are at least 18 to 20 weeks old. This is not the time to take them to dog parks, dog events, or even the park. They should remain at home in a safe, clean environment, with exposure to other healthy dogs. They should not undergo undue stress such as extended travel or intense training. This protocol will be very controversial with my colleagues. Please be advised that should you choose this protocol you accept full responsibility if your pet becomes ill.

Most veterinarians will not give such limited vaccinations. In that case, the best you might hope for would be a combination distemper, adenovirus (hepatitis), parvovirus vaccine or DAP. Some only carry a DAPP, which includes the upper respiratory virus parainfluenza. Many puppies will receive at least one vaccine, if not two or three, before you bring them home. The more vaccines they are given, the more likely they will be to develop immune system issues or allergies later in life. If possible, limit your pup to a series of two vaccines, at most.

For kittens I generally recommend a series of two distemper/herpes virus vaccines at 10 to 12 weeks and again at 14 to 16 weeks. Two vaccines are plenty, they do not need a series of three or four vaccines. If the first vaccine is not administered until 16 weeks of age, that one vaccine may be enough to give immunity. A titer can be drawn at 20 weeks to determine presence of protective antibodies if preferred.

I generally like to wait until the puppy or kitten is six to twelve months old before giving the rabies vaccine, although the vaccine is labeled as safe for use at twelve weeks of age. Again, your pet will have no protection against rabies until the vaccine is given.

If you live in a high-risk area, you may not be able to wait until six to twelve months of age to vaccinate. The first rabies vaccine will legally give a one-year duration of immunity. Each subsequent rabies vaccine will legally provide a three-year duration of immunity, no matter how long the interval from the first vaccine. Many veterinarians will only give a one-year certificate if more than one year has elapsed from the first injection. This is not appropriate! Animals with unknown vaccine history are always given a certificate showing one year of immunity when the first known rabies vaccine is given.

Multiple vaccinations should not be given at one visit, particularly for young animals. If your pet is at risk and requires more than the core vaccines for distemper, parvo, and rabies, please space out the vaccine visits. Give no more than one vaccine every two to three weeks. This will require many more visits to your veterinarian but is in the best interest for your pet's health and longevity.

When pets are adopted as adults, they do not need a full series of immunizations. Preferably, a titer can be drawn to see if any vaccinations are necessary. If the pet has already received the core vaccines from the rescue group, do not allow the pet to be given follow-up vaccines. Adult animals are quite capable of producing good immunity to parvovirus, distemper virus, and adenovirus with one injection. If in doubt, run a titer.

My current recommendations for vaccinations vary with each pet. No two pets have the same lifestyle and exposure to disease. Indoor cats are not going to be exposed to viral diseases spread by other cats, unless an unknown stray is brought into the mix or the indoor cat escapes to the great outdoors. Small dogs that use indoor piddle pads and never go outside certainly do not have the same exposure to disease that a hunting or show dog would have. Dogs in large kennel situations or spending time around shelter dogs will have a much higher rate of disease exposure.

Vaccine manufacturers are becoming more aware of client desires to vaccinate less often. Vaccinations labeled with three-year duration of immunity were developed for the core diseases of distemper, hepatitis, and parvovirus, but they were dropped from the product line because veterinarians were reluctant to switch to products that would require fewer client visits.

Governments requiring vaccination against Rabies usually have the final say in whether pets need to be vaccinated, although exemptions can be written in many states (including but not limited to Alabama, California, Colorado, Connecticut, Delaware, Florida, Illinois, Maine, Massachusetts, Maryland, New Hampshire, New Jersey, Nevada, New York, Oregon, Pennsylvania, Vermont, Virginia, and Wisconsin—this list can change) for animals with diseases that would make them poor candidates for vaccination. I consider cancer, allergic reaction to vaccines, seizures, and terminal disease to be reasons for exemption. Interestingly, when questioning veterinary oncologists (cancer specialists), they routinely felt vaccinating for infectious diseases was appropriate even for animals undergoing chemotherapy.

Vaccine labels clearly state the vaccine is to be given to "healthy dogs and cats"; pets with cancer, autoimmune disease, or other illnesses are not considered to be in good health in my opinion. Vaccines need an immune system response to work. Vaccines containing modified live viruses may cause infections in animals with a weak immune system.

I do not recommend vaccinating any animal that has ever had an allergic reaction to a vaccine. Signs of allergic reaction can include facial swelling, hives, vomiting, diarrhea, and collapse. Delayed reactions can include weakness, muscle soreness, fever, and loss of appetite. Most veterinarians will give a dose of an antihistamine or a steroid injection at the time of vaccination to deter a reaction from occurring, but I do not feel that offers enough protection to the pet. The administration of a steroid along with the vaccine may render the vaccine useless; the immune system needs to respond to the vaccine to make immunity to the disease and the steroid suppresses the immune system response. Pets with cancer or immune-mediated diseases should not have their immune system bombarded with vaccine antigens. Each pet should be evaluated as an individual to determine which, if any, vaccinations are needed.

I will give my personal feelings on vaccinations, but please take into consideration the lifestyle and exposure for your pet before making decisions for which vaccinations your own pet should receive.

Canine Distemper and Feline Panleukopenia (Distemper) Virus Vaccines—Symptoms of distemper may include coughing, sneezing, ocular and nasal discharge, pneumonia, vomiting, diarrhea, thickening of foot pads (hence the nickname "Hardpad disease"), tremors, paralysis, seizures, and death.

This is a core vaccine that most dogs and cats should receive at some point, usually as a puppy or kitten. It has been proposed that it takes a series of at least two vaccinations at least two weeks apart to get optimum immunity, however I have been challenging this theory with my vaccination protocols for puppies. If the owner desires and if the pet has a likelihood of exposure, I like to give the first vaccine at ten to twelve weeks of age and the second vaccine at fourteen to sixteen weeks of age. Individual vaccines should be given one month apart. Waiting until sixteen to eighteen weeks to vaccinate may allow the pet to make a stronger vaccine immune response.

During the first four months of life the puppy or kitten will not have good immunity against disease and should be kept away from areas where pets with unknown health status may congregate.

This includes pet stores, dog parks, fundraising events, groomers, dog and cat shows, group training, daycare, and boarding kennels.

Perform a blood titer at five to six months of age to determine whether the pet has developed protective antibodies against the disease. If the titer level is protective, no additional vaccination is necessary at that time. For many dogs and cats these two vaccines will confer lifelong immunity. It is recommended to repeat the titer one year later to confirm adult immunity.

Current research has shown these vaccines to protect against infection for four to seven years in most cases, depending on the vaccine product that is used. Titers can be performed throughout the life of the pet to determine whether protective antibodies are present. Whether to vaccinate if the titer level drops should be determined based on the health of the animal, age of the animal, exposure level, and requirements for boarding, daycare, and grooming.

Canine Adenovirus Type 2 or Hepatitis Vaccine—Luckily, this is a disease that is not seen very often. It is closely related to Canine Adenovirus Type 1, which causes upper respiratory symptoms and is included in the kennel cough vaccine. This disease often affects the eyes of the dogs, causing swelling and a blue haze in the cornea (the eyes are the window of the liver, so this makes sense in the case of hepatitis). This disease is most dangerous for dogs less than one year of age and is included in the core puppy vaccination, DAP or DAPP.

Currently, I do not perform titers for Adenovirus although they are available. I do include this vaccination in the core puppy vaccines as described under Canine Distemper Virus. Immunity probably lasts for seven years or longer; I generally do not repeat this vaccine in adult dogs belonging to clients wanting minimal vaccination for their pets.

Parvovirus Vaccine—This virus is most lethal in puppies and certain breeds which seem to be predisposed, possibly due to genetics, including Doberman Pinschers, Pit Bulls, Labrador Retrievers, and Rottweilers. Other black and tan breeds may also be more susceptible to the virus. The virus targets rapidly dividing cells, hitting hardest in the bone marrow and in the cells that line the walls of the small intestine. In very young dogs, canine parvovirus can also infect the heart, leading to inflammation of heart muscle, poor function, and arrhythmias.

Symptoms often associated with canine parvovirus include lethargy, depression, and loss or lack of appetite, followed by a sudden onset of high fever, vomiting, and diarrhea. The virus itself is not necessarily the cause of death. Death occurs due to dehydration and sepsis by bacteria entering the bloodstream from the damaged intestines. Environmental stress, parasite infestation, and concurrent bacterial or viral infections also contribute to a high mortality rate.

For this disease I recommend two vaccinations given about four weeks apart in puppies at the same time as the distemper vaccination if the veterinarian does not carry separate distemper and parvo vaccines. There are individual vaccines available that contain only the Parvo virus, but currently there are no individual distemper vaccinations available. A Parvovirus blood titer should be run at five to six months to confirm immunity and be repeated annually if proof is needed for boarding, daycare, grooming, or training. If the parvo titer is low, an individual vaccination for parvovirus can be given.

As with distemper and hepatitis, puppies under four months of age have not developed good protection and should not be exposed to group situations with dogs of unknown health. Parvovirus is highly contagious. Any dogs that are ill should be isolated and cared for by one caretaker to eliminate spread of the disease.

Disinfect any materials used to care for those dogs with a solution of a half cup of chlorine bleach mixed with one gallon of water.

Leptospirosis Vaccine—This is one of the most reactive vaccines on the market. Many dogs will have allergic reactions including hives, facial swelling, vomiting, diarrhea, and difficulty breathing. These reactions occur most commonly in small breeds of dogs. For that reason, I do not recommend this vaccine for dogs weighing less than ten pounds, unless they live in a high-risk situation.

Leptospirosis is a disease caused by a spirochete, a type of bacterium. It is spread through the urine of infected animals, most commonly rats, raccoons, foxes, skunks, and dairy cattle. It can be found in contaminated stagnant water and streams and survives well in hot, humid environments. Outbreaks have occurred in cities due to high rat populations. Leptospirosis is also zoonotic, meaning the disease can be transmitted from animals to humans.

Leptospirosis is treatable with antibiotics and intravenous fluids, if diagnosed in time. The most common symptoms are related to kidney and liver failure, including increased thirst and urination, decreased appetite, fever, bloody urine, and yellow skin (jaundice). The old name for this disease was "Red Water Disease" due to the bloody urine that is often seen with this disease. Currently there are seven sub-varieties of Leptospirosis that can be diagnosed in dogs. The old vaccines protected against two of the serovars and the newer vaccines protect against four of the serovars.

There is no good reason to perform annual titers for Leptospirosis once the pet is vaccinated because the vaccine only confers immunity for nine to twelve months. If a pet is at high risk for exposure to Leptospirosis, vaccination should be performed annually. High-risk pets include hunting dogs, dogs in urban areas with a high rat population, and dogs that go camping or hiking with their owners in wilderness areas. During my thirty years in practice, I have diagnosed Leptospirosis only a handful of times, although it seems to be more common recently in small pockets across the country. Currently, city dogs with exposure to rat urine may be at most risk. (I recommend putting boots on your dog when walking in the city.)

Parainfluenza Virus and Bordetella (canine or feline) Vaccine—
These are upper respiratory diseases that are highly contagious and are spread through nasal secretions. Symptoms of disease include sneezing, coughing, lethargy, fever, and lack of appetite. These are two of the causes of Tracheobronchitis or Kennel Cough. This illness does not cause death and is roughly equivalent to the human cold. While Kennel Cough can be irritating and inconvenient, it is not lethal.

I do not recommend routinely vaccinating for this. However, dogs or cats that are taken to boarding kennels, groomers, shows, and other high-pet-population events will most likely be required to have this vaccine. It is not highly reactive but does stimulate the immune system and some dogs and cats will have adverse reactions.

Many pets will develop symptoms of Kennel Cough, lasting three to ten days, when given the vaccine and can shed the organisms for one to seven weeks after vaccination. Group venues that require vaccination for "kennel cough" should require that oral or nasal vaccines be given at least two to four weeks prior to the event to minimize shedding of the organisms. Subcutaneous (injection under the skin) vaccination is not recommended and does not confer immunity as well as the oral or nasal vaccines.

This is an annual vaccine, conferring immunity for no more than six to twelve months. There are no titers available.

Giving this vaccine does not guarantee that your pet will not get Kennel Cough but may lessen the symptoms. I recommend finding groomers that do not require the vaccine, do not house large numbers of pets in a confined space, or one that will come to your house. Find a boarding kennel that is clean, has good ventilation, and does not require the vaccine, leave your pets with friends, or find a good house sitter to stay with your pets.

Canine Coronavirus Vaccine—This is a highly contagious intestinal virus that causes vomiting, diarrhea, fever, lethargy, and loss of appetite. This disease is not as lethal as Parvovirus but can commonly be found in pets also infected with Parvovirus. When not associated with Parvovirus, disease caused by Coronavirus is generally self-limiting. Puppies are the most susceptible to this virus; death occurs due to dehydration when treatment is not administered early in the course of the disease. Coronavirus is not considered a core vaccine and it is not recommended that dogs be routinely given this vaccine. I do not use or recommend this vaccine. The intestinal form of Coronavirus in dogs is not associated with the respiratory form of illness in people.

Canine or Feline Giardia Vaccine—Giardia is a parasite that is transmitted through infested water or food contaminated with feces. It is seen most often in large kennel situations, multiple pet households, or dirty environments. The most common cause of infection is drinking from a contaminated lake, pond, or stream.

Infection with Giardia can cause chronic vomiting, diarrhea, loss of appetite, and weight loss. Giardia is treatable with anti-parasitic medications such as Metronidazole and Fenbendazole. Adding food-grade diatomaceous earth to the diet for thirty days will help eliminate the parasite. (Dose is one teaspoon to one tablespoon per day, depending on size of pet.) The key to preventing Giardia is diagnosis, treatment, and cleanliness, as well as having a healthy immune system. Most cases of Giardia that I see are pet store puppies with weak immune systems, multi-pet households, and dogs exposed to stagnant water.

Giardia can also infect humans. My son had Giardia when he was two years old; treatment lasted four weeks. I am pretty sure they have better ways to treat this now but thirty years ago he had to drink liquid Furazolidone, which has now been shown to be carcinogenic and is no longer available in the United States. I have never had a pet infected with Giardia, so my son had to have picked it up in the environment. Guess we should have been better about the hand washing! Unfortunately, just like many pets that have been infected with giardia, my son has had a life-long battle with bowel issues including bacterial overgrowth.

I do not recommend using the Giardia vaccine. It can be reactive and the easiest way to prevent Giardia is to test and treat any new animal coming into the household. Test stool samples twice a year, making sure Giardia testing is included. Normal fecal flotation testing may not pick up Giardia. Keep water bowls clean and avoid stagnant water in the environment.

Canine Influenza Vaccine—The Canine Influenza Virus is not the same as the Parainfluenza Virus related to Hepatitis (the Adenovirus). Influenza virus H3N8 was originally diagnosed in Greyhounds in Florida in 2004 and the first vaccine was released in 2009. The H3N8 Influenza virus jumped from horses to dogs where the animals were housed together at racetracks. This virus does not transmit to humans. Because Greyhounds are shipped all over the country, this virus can now be found in most states.

Just as with any illness, most dogs with a good immune system will either remain healthy or have a short illness with flu-like symptoms. A small percentage of dogs will develop pneumonia with a high fever and may succumb to the disease. The severe outbreaks that have occurred have been in high population, high stress facilities such as pet stores that sell puppies, puppy mills, boarding kennels, and veterinary hospitals with many sick animals.

A second strain of Influenza, H3N2, was first detected in dogs in Korea in 2007. The virus originally jumped from birds to dogs. It was first diagnosed in dogs in the United States in 2015 and can now be found in most states. In 2017 there was a large outbreak associated with a dog show in Georgia; dogs on the show circuit traveled to many states, carrying the virus, resulting in a multi-state outbreak.

Neither strain is transmissible from dogs to humans. The signs of this illness in dogs are cough, runny nose, fever, lethargy, eye discharge, and reduced appetite, but not all dogs will show signs of illness. The severity of illness associated with Canine Influenza in dogs can range from no signs to severe illness resulting in pneumonia and sometimes death.

Influenza has an incubation period of 1 to 5 days, with clinical signs in most cases appearing 2 to 3 days after exposure. Dogs infected with influenza may start showing respiratory signs between 2 and 8 days after infection. Dogs are most contagious during the incubation period and shed the virus even though they are not showing clinical signs of illness.

The virus is spread through respiratory and oral secretions. The virus can remain viable (alive and able to infect) on surfaces for up to 48 hours, on clothing for 24 hours, and on hands for 12 hours.

Many groomers, kennels, and high-density pet centers have started to require this vaccine for admission. The current influenza vaccine combines the H3N8 and the H3N2 strains of virus. I do not recommend giving this vaccine. Again, finding a small, clean kennel or groomer with good ventilation, or having someone come to your home are better choices.

Rattlesnake Vaccine—A rattlesnake's venom is meant to kill its prey. Most rattlesnakes' venom disrupts the integrity of the victim's blood vessels, resulting in pain, tissue damage, and internal bleeding. If the bite is on the throat or face, the resultant swelling can cause death due to airway closure, as well. Some rattlesnakes have neurotoxic venom, which attacks the nervous system and results in paralysis. Many dogs die each year from rattlesnake bites, and many more are permanently injured. Red Rock Biologics provides a rattlesnake vaccine for dogs. It was approved by the United States Department of Agriculture in 2004. This vaccine is designed to help the dog develop antibodies in response to the appearance of rattlesnake venom in the body. These antibodies can result in less pain and tissue damage at the site of the bite, more time to get to a veterinary clinic after a bite, and potentially less need for antivenom and other treatment.

This vaccine protects against the venom of the Western Diamondback rattlesnake. It may provide some degree of cross-protection for the venom of several related rattlesnakes, such as the Western rattlesnake, Sidewinder, Timber rattlesnake, Massasauga rattlesnake, Copperhead, and Eastern Diamondback rattlesnake. This vaccine does not protect against the venom of the water moccasin, Mojave rattlesnake, or Coral snake according to the manufacturer.

The vaccine is not fully protective; it will not completely mitigate the effects of a rattlesnake bite. How well it works for a dog that is bitten by a rattlesnake depends on the type of snake, the amount of venom delivered during the bite, the size of the dog, the size and age of the snake, and the location of the bite. However, dogs that are bitten by the types of rattlesnakes listed above often experience less pain and swelling, with a faster recovery, when they have been previously vaccinated.

Snakebite is always an emergency, even if the dog has received the rattlesnake vaccine. The effectiveness of the rattlesnake vaccine can be increased by adhering to the following guidelines:

- A dog's first dose of rattlesnake vaccine should be given no sooner than four months of age. This is because the safety of the vaccine has not been evaluated in younger puppies.
- The first time your dog is given the rattlesnake vaccine, it needs to be re-administered in one month. Very small and very large dogs may require a third booster in this initial sequence.

The vaccine is most protective about four to six weeks following its administration. Its effectiveness slowly declines after that. In areas of the country where rattlesnakes are active for only part of the year, a single vaccine given about one month before the start of the "rattlesnake season" is probably sufficient. This is usually early spring. In areas where rattlesnakes are active all year, your veterinarian may recommend boosters every four to six months.

Side effects may include mild swelling at the site of the vaccine injection. More serious allergic reactions resulting in vomiting, diarrhea, and lethargy are even rarer. Very serious allergic reactions including anaphylaxis have only been reported in one to three dogs per million vaccines given.

The rattlesnake vaccine should only be given to healthy dogs. I have never lived in an area with rattlesnakes therefore I have no experience with the use of this vaccine.

Canine Lyme Disease—Lyme disease is transmitted by ticks. The Borrelia bacteria that cause Lyme disease are commonly found in field mice and deer; the most common vectors for transmission are the Deer Tick and other closely related ticks. The ticks are most active from early spring to late fall, but symptoms may take two to five months to show up after infection, so disease can be diagnosed any time during the year. Up to 95% of infected dogs will never show any symptoms of disease. This has caused great controversy over whether dogs with positive tests should be treated with antibiotics if they are asymptomatic. Dogs that have positive tests may have protective antibodies and never need treatment. Personally, I only like to treat dogs that are symptomatic with a positive test.

Symptoms generally include loss of appetite, lethargy, mild fever, swollen joints, lameness, painful muscles, and occasionally digestive upset. More severe cases result in kidney failure and heart disease.

My mother's first Doberman had the cardiac form of the disease. It was early in my veterinary career and Lyme disease was new to the veterinary world. I wanted to sedate the dog for a dental cleaning. During the preoperative work-up I performed an electrocardiogram, which revealed an abnormal heartbeat. Lab work revealed she was positive for Lyme disease, even though she had no other symptoms. I treated her with Doxycycline for a month and her arrhythmia cleared. Her dental was performed with no complications.

There have also been reported cases of seizures and other neurologic symptoms secondary to Borrelia infection, which I have seen and treated successfully.

I do not recommend vaccinating against Lyme disease. Most dogs exposed to ticks carrying Lyme disease do not develop symptoms (although there are isolated pockets in the United States where a high percentage of exposed dogs will become symptomatic). The tick must be attached and feeding on the dog for at least twelve hours, and more likely 24 to 48 hours, to transmit the infective Borrelia organisms.

The most effective way to avoid Lyme disease is to avoid tick infestation. Keeping grass cut, bushes trimmed, and checking daily for ticks during tick season, can be your best defense. There are many chemical and natural products available to keep ticks off pets. Obviously, I prefer natural products. No product is 100% guaranteed to keep your pets tick-free, so daily tick checks are essential if you live in a high tick area.

Lyme disease is very treatable when diagnosed early; however, do not ignore symptoms! The symptoms of Lyme disease are associated with the immune system's reaction to the Borrelia organism. Antigen-antibody complexes (particles of the infectious organism linked to the immune particles attacking them) are deposited in the joints and kidneys, causing much of the problem. Vaccination may contribute to this problem. The human Lyme vaccine was pulled from the market due to debate about it potentially causing immune-mediated polyarthritis.

Vaccination is not 100% effective and is only helpful in dogs that have not already been exposed to Borrelia. It is estimated that the vaccine is 80% effective in dogs with no previous exposure to Borrelia, but only 60% effective in dogs with prior exposure. If you really want to vaccinate, a negative test showing no antibodies in the system would be a good idea and vaccination should be started when the dog is less than four months old.

Many times, I get results showing good immunity due to vaccination, when the pet has never been vaccinated. That means they have essentially vaccinated themselves by having a proper response to exposure to the natural organism.

There are at least ten tick-borne diseases that can affect dogs, including Anaplasmosis, Rocky Mountain Spotted Fever, Ehrlichiosis, Babesiosis, Bartonellosis, Tularemia, Hepatozoonosis, Rickettsiosis, and Tick Paralysis. While Lyme Disease seems to be the most commonly diagnosed infection, vaccinations do not exist for any tick-borne disease except Lyme Disease. The obvious answer is to keep your pet from becoming infested with ticks, not to prevent only one disease but many.

Feline Viral Rhinotracheitis Vaccine (Herpes Virus 1)—Herpes virus 1 causes upper respiratory disease and conjunctivitis in cats. Once infected, the cat will always be a carrier of the virus, just like herpes virus infections in humans. When cats are subjected to stresses such as vaccination, overcrowding, travel, or concurrent illnesses the Herpes virus will become active, bringing out symptoms of disease and/or shedding of the virus.

The most common chronic symptoms seen in practice are conjunctivitis and corneal ulceration. This can be very painful and can lead to blindness or perforation and loss of the eye if not treated aggressively. The FVRCP vaccine includes herpes virus 1 (FVR) and is given in the nose or by injection under the skin. Kittens have the highest risk of infection. Vaccination will not prevent shedding of the virus and vaccinated cats can still become ill with a mild form of the disease. I generally include this vaccination in a series of two kitten vaccines when they are vaccinated for Panleukopenia.

Feline Calicivirus Vaccine—Several strains of Feline Calicivirus (FCV) circulate in domestic and wild cats. The virus mutates readily, leading to new strains that may not be fully covered by existing vaccines. Strains vary in the severity of the disease that they cause, with the majority causing only mild disease. The ability of the virus to mutate likely explains why after 40 years of vaccinating against FCV, outbreaks still frequently occur. There is a vaccination called Calicivax for the severe strain, which should only be used for cats in shelter or very high population situations.

The virus spreads through direct contact with the saliva, nasal mucous, and eye discharge of infected cats and through aerosol droplets that spread when cats sneeze. Lab tests have also detected the virus in urine, feces, and blood. Cats typically shed the virus for about two or three weeks after infection, but some cats become long-term carriers, and continue to shed the virus on and off for months. After being exposed to FCV, the incubation period is 2 to 14 days before symptoms appear.

Calicivirus causes upper respiratory infection, stomatitis, and gingivitis (inflammation and ulceration of the mouth and gums). Fever, lethargy, and loss of appetite are common symptoms. These symptoms can persist from 5 to 10 days in mild cases and up to six weeks in more severe ones. Kittens are most susceptible to this disease; infected animals will most likely remain carriers for life. Rarely is the milder form of this virus life-threatening and immunity, once vaccinated, probably lasts for years. This is included in the series of kitten vaccines given in the first few months of life, along with the Distemper (Panleukopenia) and Feline Viral Rhinotracheitis vaccination. I do not recommend vaccination of adult cats. This virus is resistant to most disinfectants and can remain in the environment for days to weeks. The key to prevention is vaccination of young kittens, keeping a clean environment, and isolating any new cats coming into a colony for a minimum of three weeks to make sure they do not develop any symptoms.

Feline Chlamydia Vaccine—Chlamydia is a bacterium that causes coughing, sneezing, runny eyes and nose, conjunctivitis, and upper respiratory symptoms. Occasionally kittens will develop pneumonia. This infection is seen mostly in kittens, shelters, and high stress living environments. Transmission can take place even without direct contact with an infected animal, as the molecules from a cough or sneeze can travel across a room, a human caretaker can carry the bacteria and spread it by touch, or the cat may come in contact with a contaminated object, such as in a bedding or feeding area.

The Chlamydia vaccination will not prevent infection but may reduce symptoms of disease. Side effects from the vaccination are common, including fever, loss of appetite, lameness, and lethargy. This disease does have zoonotic potential (can be transmitted to humans). It is uncomfortable and annoying but is rarely life-threatening. I do not recommend the use of this vaccine.

Feline Leukemia Vaccine—Feline Leukemia Virus is spread through nasal secretions and saliva. Kittens are much more susceptible to the virus, as are males and cats that have outdoor access. Kittens can contract the virus in utero from the mother cat. Some kittens will convert to negative status within three months of birth, while others will still test positive, and some will die shortly after birth. The average life expectancy after contracting the disease is less than three years. Cats usually develop anemia (low red blood cell count), cancer, and secondary infections due to immune deficiency.

Cats with Feline Leukemia may not show any signs, even for years. Some of the more common symptoms of feline leukemia include anemia, lethargy, progressive weight loss, secondary infections, persistent diarrhea, poor coat condition, fever, generalized weakness, gingivitis, stomatitis, lymphoma, and fibrosarcoma formation.

Cats must be in direct or intimate contact to contract the disease. Indoor cats in a closed colony that test negative for the disease do not have opportunity to be exposed to the virus. Indoor cats should not be vaccinated for Feline Leukemia unless the owner is likely to bring in untested stray cats. Owners should have all new cats tested for Feline Leukemia and Feline Immunodeficiency Virus before exposing them to cats already in the household. If a stray cat is brought into a closed colony, the cat should be isolated; testing should be performed immediately and repeated in three months, as any recent exposure may not show up before that length of time.

The length of duration of immunity from this vaccine is currently unknown and the recommendation is to repeat the vaccination annually. I personally believe the duration of immunity is much longer, but there is no proof of that. Not all cats will achieve protection even when given the vaccine. For outdoor cats with exposure to stray cats, testing and vaccinating with a series of two vaccinations three weeks apart is recommended.

This vaccine has been incriminated in causing fibrosarcoma tumors at the site of injection. Insist it be given as low as possible on the hind leg (preferably the left, as we like to give rabies vaccines in the right hind leg).

Feline Infectious Peritonitis Vaccine—There are still many questions about the transmission of this disease, which is caused by a Coronavirus. Some cats exposed to this strain of Coronavirus do not become ill, some become carriers that shed the virus, and others become sick and die (a small percentage). This is a disease commonly associated with large cat colonies, stressful conditions, or cats suffering from concurrent diseases. The highest incidence is found in kittens three months to three years of age, with incidence decreasing sharply after cats reach three years of age, when the immune system is stronger. Likewise, older cats with weakened immune systems are also more likely to acquire this disease. This is not the same Coronavirus strain as COVID19.

Symptoms of Feline Infectious Peritonitis vary depending upon the strain of virus involved, the status of the cat's immune system, and the organs affected. There are two forms reported, including wet (effusive form), which targets the body cavities, and dry (non-effusive form), which targets the various organs. The wet form tends to progress more rapidly than the dry form. Symptoms may include fever, loss of appetite, weight loss, diarrhea, rough hair coat, respiratory distress, liver failure, kidney failure, and death.

The intranasal vaccine should only be used in cats that have never been exposed to Coronavirus, which limits the use of the vaccine. This vaccine is of minimal, if any, benefit and is currently not recommended for use.

Feline Immunodeficiency Virus Vaccine—This vaccine has been discontinued. Feline Immunodeficiency Virus is transmitted primarily through bite wounds and is seen mostly in outdoor male cats that fight with other cats. FIV is not necessarily a death sentence, as many cats can be carriers of the virus for years with no signs of illness. There are five strains of virus that cause FIV, but the vaccine protects against only two strains and does not protect against the most common strain found in the United States. Once a cat is vaccinated with this product, the cat will always test positive for the FIV virus. If a cat is picked up as a stray and tested at a shelter facility, there is no way to know if the cat has been vaccinated or infected. This could result in cats being euthanized as infected cats when they were not infected. This vaccine also contains adjuvants, which are the vaccine additives incriminated in causing vaccine related tumors.

Feline Ringworm Vaccine—Ringworm is a fungal skin infection seen commonly in cats and kittens living in crowded unsanitary conditions. Like any fungus, ringworm species grow best in dark, damp conditions and are sensitive to sunlight and drying. Cats with compromised immune systems, such as young kittens or those infected with Feline Leukemia or Feline Immunodeficiency Virus, are more likely to contract ringworm (named for the ring-like lesions on the skin).

Cats can be asymptomatic carriers of the fungal organisms, particularly long-haired cats. This vaccine should only be given to healthy cats over four months of age and consists of a series of three injections over two months. The vaccine only protects against one of the three strains of ringworm fungus that affect cats. The vaccine is controversial since it may decrease the appearance of clinical lesions without preventing infection, increasing the number of carrier cats. Field studies have shown only two-week duration of immunity when the vaccine is used for prevention or treatment. I do not recommend ever using this vaccine. Good hygiene, clean living conditions, grooming, strengthening the immune system, and exposure to sunlight, will help prevent this disease.

Dogs can contract ringworm, however there is no canine ringworm vaccine.

Rabies Vaccination

In almost all cases, rabies virus is deadly to any pet or person contracting the disease. Because of the zoonotic potential threat to humans and the almost certain death from the disease, most municipalities and states in the United States require vaccination and licensing of pets with required proof of current vaccination. People in the United States rarely die of Rabies because of the vaccination requirements. In third-world countries where vaccination is done less commonly, thousands of people die from rabies every year.

The most common transmission to humans in the United States comes from exposure to bats. Rabies virus is transmitted from saliva to blood through open wounds (most specifically bite wounds) but has been transmitted through mucous membranes such as the gums and conjunctiva (tissue surrounding the eyes). Rabies virus travels from the wound along nerve pathways to the brain where infection and inflammation eventually kill the host.

Dogs and cats are vaccinated for rabies beginning any time after three months of age. The first vaccine is valid for one year and pets must receive a booster vaccination at the end of that one-year period. The second vaccination will be good for three years, providing a product approved for three-year duration is used. (There are some one-year vaccines on the market.) Even if more than one year has elapsed from the initial vaccination, the second vaccination is still valid for three years.

There has been an ongoing discussion regarding the actual duration of immunity for rabies vaccination. The rabies vaccination challenge study spearheaded by Dr. Jean Dodds of Hemopet Labs, has shown the vaccination gives protection from disease for three years, but immunologic testing showed declining titers in the fourth and fifth years (Rabies Challenge Fund). A positive titer showing antibodies in sufficient levels can be used as proof of protection, but once the titer drops it is unknown if the animals have immunologic memory if challenged with the virus. Unfortunately, because of the zoonotic threat of this disease, changes in vaccination protocol may never happen.

One of the worst problems I have seen with the three-year vaccination protocol has been veterinarians signing vaccination certificates stating two-year duration of immunity when a three-year vaccine has been administered. This is just another way to get pets back into the office more frequently, giving unnecessary vaccines. Always ask for a vaccine with three-year duration of immunity; make certain that the certificate states three-year duration as well. There are no two-year vaccines in existence. This vaccination should never be given at the same time as other vaccines. Make the effort to wait at least one month between vaccinations if multiple vaccines need to be given.

Because rabies is a vaccine that travels along nerve pathways, I do not recommend that this vaccine be given to pets with seizure or nerve disorders. One disorder that I personally think is related to the rabies vaccination is Eosinophilic Myositis of the masseter and temporalis muscles (the chewing muscles on the head). Dogs with this disease will develop pain and inflammation in those muscles and the muscles will atrophy (shrink) until the top of the head has the appearance of a skull covered with skin. I see this most commonly in Golden Retrievers, but it can occur in any breed and is reported commonly in Doberman Pinschers, German Shepherds, Labrador Retrievers, and Cavalier King Charles Spaniels. Symptoms are usually seen ten days to two months after the rabies vaccine is given. (Think how long it takes for the virus to travel from the hind end of the pet, where the vaccine should be given, to the head.) Treatment for this disease in the past has included high doses of steroids to decrease inflammation. I have never seen this treatment cure the disease, but it does make the dogs more comfortable while the process of muscle atrophy is taking place. Affected dogs have shown a greater response to acupuncture and herbal therapy, in my experience, than to steroids.

The Rabies vaccine has been incriminated for causing fibrosarcoma tumors at the site of injection. An adjuvant is added to the vaccine to stimulate a more robust immune response. Some of the most common adjuvants include aluminum hydroxide, aluminum phosphate and calcium phosphate. Adjuvanted vaccines can cause more local reactions (such as redness, swelling, and pain at the injection site) and more systemic reactions (such as fever, chills, and body aches) than non-adjuvanted vaccines. The World Health Organization named aluminum hydroxide, a component of many veterinary vaccines, a grade 3 carcinogen (out of 4). The veterinary vaccines that include these carcinogenic adjuvants include Rabies, Leptospirosis, and Lyme.

One preservative, thimerosal—an ethyl mercury derivative, is thought to contribute to tumor formation. I recommend insisting on a "T-free" or "thimerosal-free" rabies vaccine. Most veterinarians are not aware this vaccine exists. It only costs a few cents more per dose which is worth the investment.

MY RECOMMENDED VACCINATION PROTOCOL

My recommended vaccination protocol (under ideal circumstances in a closed colony where no new animals are being introduced that may be sick or carrying disease, as in a home environment):

For dogs:

- DAP (distemper, adenovirus, parvovirus) vaccine should be administered to puppies at 12 and 16 weeks, if the puppies are in a clean, healthy environment with no exposure to sick dogs. For those desiring the least vaccines possible, I have had success giving a single distemper vaccine at 13 to 14 weeks with a single parvo vaccine at 16 to 17 weeks. This must be followed with a titer one month later to confirm sufficient immunity. Most veterinarians will not give single vaccines. If following this protocol, remember you assume all risk if your pet should become ill.

- Dogs older than six months when first vaccinated will most likely not require a second vaccine booster four weeks later, although I have seen many recommendations for a series of three to four vaccines in a series. If the vaccine status of the dog is unknown it is best to begin with a titer; protective antibodies may already be present meaning no vaccination is necessary.

- Draw blood for distemper and parvo titers at 5 to 6 months of age and annually, thereafter, if needed for boarding, daycare, grooming, show, or training. Give a booster vaccine for parvo if the titer is low. I continue running titers for life, as dogs are constantly exposed to other dogs outside and we currently have no way to measure memory cell immunity.

☐ Rabies vaccine should be administered at 6 months to 1 year of age; repeat 1 year later with a vaccine good for 3-year duration, then every 3 years provided the pet is healthy enough to be vaccinated (based on state requirements). Ask for a T-free vaccine. The dog must be kept under close supervision until vaccination to minimize exposure. Titers can be run to determine immune status, but most municipalities and states do not recognize titers for licensing requirements. This is changing slowly in some areas.

☐ Lifestyle vaccines (Bordetella, Influenza, Lyme, Leptospirosis, Rattlesnake, etc.) should only be administered if your pet lives in a high-risk environment. As explained under the individual vaccines discussed, I rarely advise these vaccines. I recommend finding boarding, daycare, and grooming services that do not require every vaccine imaginable. Having in-home care is much safer for your dog.

For cats:

☐ FVRCP should be administered at 12 and 16 weeks of age if the kittens are in a clean, healthy environment with no exposure to sick cats. If the kitten is older than 16 weeks at the time of first vaccination, a second vaccine may not be necessary, as the immune system is more robust by this age.

☐ Draw blood for panleukopenia (distemper) titer at 6 months of age and annually, thereafter, if needed for proof of vaccine status for boarding or grooming. This may not be necessary for adult cats housed indoors in a closed colony where no new cats will be introduced, provided the titers at 6 and 18 months of age show good immunity.

☐ Rabies should be administered at 6 months to 1 year of age; repeat 1 year later with a vaccine good for 3-year duration, then every 3 years provided the pet is healthy enough to be vaccinated (based on state requirements). Ask for a T-free vaccine. I do not vaccinate indoor cats after the second vaccine provided the owners are responsible and do not allow their cats outside at all. Titers can be run to determine immune status, but most municipalities and states do not recognize titers for licensing requirements. Bats can be carriers of the rabies virus. If a bat gets in the house, there is no way to tell if your pet has been bitten. Keep this in mind if you decide not to vaccinate an indoor cat. One option would be to run a titer if a bat is found in the home to make sure the cat is protected.

Vaccines should never be given to a pet that is sick, undergoing surgery or any anesthetic procedure, undergoing chemotherapy, or suffers from chronic inflammatory diseases. If the veterinarian requires vaccinations to have a procedure performed, the vaccines should be given a minimum of two, preferably four, weeks prior to the procedure.

Cancer can and does cause immune compromise and stress on the immune system. Vaccination causes the immune system to respond. There is no need to add additional stress to the immune system of a pet fighting cancer. Of course, oncologists also believe it is safe to use harmful chemicals for flea, tick, and heartworm prevention when pets are receiving chemotherapy. I disagree with that, as well.

Vaccinations should be spaced at least two to three weeks apart. Avoid having multiple vaccines given at one time. Ask to have vaccines given low on the hind legs. We have designated areas for vaccines in case a reaction or tumor appears; this gives us information we can use in the future. Some practitioners have advocated giving vaccines in the tail of cats; I have yet to try this as cats are loaded with weapons that they might use to pierce my body parts if I make them mad enough.

Side effects from vaccination can occur. They may include:

- pain at the injection site
- fever
- lethargy
- lameness
- vomiting
- diarrhea
- anaphylactic reaction
- hives
- swelling

- tumor formation
- shock
- death

Side effects usually start appearing within a few minutes to hours after the vaccination, but they can also take days, and even years, to appear. The most severe reactions are generally apparent within a few minutes. Most vaccine reactions are never reported to vaccine manufacturers, and many are never reported to the veterinarian administering the vaccine. This contributes to the belief that vaccines are harmless. If you suspect your pet has had a reaction, please be sure to have that added to the medical records.

Homeopathic vaccine remedies

I am not trained in homeopathy; however, the following remedies are commonly recommended at the time of vaccination to decrease side effects:

- **Ledum palustre** (the homeopathic puncture-wound remedy) at a dose of 30c.
- **Belladonna** at a dose of 30c is beneficial for swelling and fever that may come that night.
- **Thuja occidentalis** at a dose of 30c can help to ease various side effects of a vaccine.
- **Apis Mellifica** at a dose of 30c if there is any facial swelling.
- **Lyssin** at a dose of 30c when rabies vaccination is given. Some veterinarians recommend a single dose on the day of vaccination however some recommend a more prolonged course of therapy:

  Lyssin should be given for 3 days prior to the rabies vaccine, on the day of the vaccine, and for one week after.

- Dogs 100 pounds to 150 pounds: 5 pellets in one dose daily
- Dogs 50 pounds to 100 pounds: 4 pellets in one dose daily
- Dogs 15 to 25 pounds: 3 pellets in one dose daily
- Cats, and Dogs under 15 pounds: 2 pellets in one dose daily

More Methods to Detox your Pet Following Vaccination

Give high-quality probiotics. Over 80% of the immune system resides in the gut. A healthy microbiome (gut bacteria) can help the overwhelm that occurs in the immune system when vaccines are given.

Include prebiotics with the probiotics. Prebiotics are the food source for the good bacteria in the gut. Prebiotics include soluble fibers that ferment in the gut. Sources include fructo-oligosaccharides (FOS), Mannan oligosaccharides (MOS), Galacto-oligosaccarides (GOS), and inulin. Natural sources of prebiotics include mushrooms, chicory root, and dandelion greens. Dandelion greens have the added benefit of draining toxins from the liver and kidneys.

Add omega-3 fatty acids to your pet's meal. High-quality fish oils can decrease inflammation in the body. Fish oil should be bought in dark glass or aluminum bottles and stored in a cool, dark area. Fish oils should not be stored in plastic containers, as chemicals can leach into the oil from the plastic. Oils will go rancid quickly if exposed to heat, air, and sunlight. Rancid oils are worse than no oils, as they promote inflammation in the body. Fish oil should not have a strong fishy odor. Recommended doses are 30 to 60 mg of DHA (docosahexaenoic acid) and EPA (eicosapentaenoic acid) added together per pound of body weight daily.

Add things to the diet that can help bind the metals found in the vaccines. Chlorella, bentonite clay, seaweed, brussels sprouts, cabbage, cauliflower, and cilantro are great choices for this. Add any combination of these in small amounts to the diet for two to four weeks following vaccination. Vegetables should be finely ground or steamed to help break down cell walls in the plants for better digestion and absorption.

Give CoenzymeQ10 (CoQ10), Quercetin, or ubiquinol as an antioxidant to decrease inflammation. Dosing can range from one to five milligrams per pound of body weight once or twice daily. My dogs take this daily; I use the higher dose since my dogs are breeds prone to heart disease.

16

Parasites and Parasite Prevention

Dogs and cats can harbor intestinal parasites, external parasites, and heartworms. Intestinal worms can be a serious problem in young puppies and kittens. In adult dogs, intestinal parasites are only occasionally life-threatening. Debilitated animals or those that have a weakened immune system are more likely to experience severe intestinal parasitism and show clinical signs due to their worms; they are also likely to be infected with multiple parasites at the same time. Healthy animals are less likely to be plagued by these invaders. Regular testing to determine whether parasites are living inside your pet should be performed at least once per year, preferably twice. Regular grooming will help detect any external parasites (fleas, ticks, lice). My raw-fed, minimally vaccinated dogs, cats, and horses have never had issues with parasite infestation.

INTESTINAL PARASITES

There are many types of intestinal parasites that exist. Diarrhea is the most common symptom and may include stools containing blood or mucous. Severe infestations may result in loss of appetite and weight loss. Take a fresh stool sample to your veterinarian to be checked for parasites at least twice per year or any time your pet has loose stools for more than a day. If parasites are detected, be sure to take a stool sample after completing treatment to be sure the parasites have been cleared. Multi-drug-resistance is becoming more common which means multiple treatments may be required. All pets in the home should be tested, as they may easily transmit parasites to each other.

Tapeworms—Tapeworms are transmitted through ingestion of fleas or small rodents (mice, rabbits). They are flat, segmented worms that attach to the intestinal wall. As the adult worms mature, individual segments of the worm break off and are passed in the stool intermittently. The segments may be seen around the anus or on the feces that is passed. They are about half an inch long and look like grains of rice or cucumber seeds. Because the segments pass intermittently, they may not be found on routine laboratory testing and are more often found by seeing segments on the pet or in the stool. Tapeworms cannot be passed directly from pet to pet or pet to person; they must go through the intermediate host—the flea or mouse. Treatment consists of oral or injectable medication; one dose is sufficient, unless the dog or cat has continued exposure to fleas or hunts small prey.

Roundworms—These are very common in puppies and kittens. A typical pot-bellied appearance occurs in young animals with severe infestation. Adult worms are four to six inches long, round, and white. They can be passed in feces or vomit. The adult roundworms mate in the intestines; the female worm lays thousands of eggs per day which are shed in the feces into the environment. The eggs become infective in two to four weeks in the environment. When the eggs are ingested, they hatch in the intestine, penetrate the intestinal wall, and travel via the blood to the liver and then to the lungs. From the lungs, the larvae can ascend the trachea and travel to the intestine to mature into adults or into the blood vessels where they travel to muscles and organs, a condition known as larva migrans.

Humans can also become infected with roundworms and develop larva migrans. This condition in humans is typically associated with the eye. Infection commonly occurs when children eat dirt containing infectious eggs. It is important to keep children's sandboxes covered to keep cats and wildlife from defecating in the sand.

Puppies and kittens can be infected with roundworms through the milk of their infected mother or through the umbilical vein (dogs only) to the liver and lungs of the newborn. At the time of birth, when the lungs inflate, the larvae burst out and travel to the intestines where they mature in three weeks.

Roundworm eggs are extremely resistant to common disinfectants, including bleach, and environmental changes (heat and cold). Eggs can survive for years in the environment.

Treatment consists of oral medication repeated in two weeks.

Hookworms—These worms are shaped like a hook and are about half an inch in length. Hookworms have three sets of teeth which enables them to attach to the wall of the small intestine where the parasite drinks blood from the host animal. Hookworm infestation may result in anemia (low red blood cell count). Adult hookworms mate in the intestine where the females lay large numbers of eggs which are passed in the feces into the environment. Within ten days, the eggs will develop into infective larvae that can infect a new host through ingestion or skin penetration. Hookworms that enter through the skin migrate to the lungs, enter the trachea, and are swallowed into the intestines. They also can migrate into muscles and organs throughout the body and become encased in a cyst. Puppies can become infected through the mother's milk, but not through the umbilical vein.

Hookworms can infect humans. The most well-known form of infection is cutaneous larva migrans, commonly known as "creeping eruption". This results in red, itchy patches on the skin. It is seen most in hot, humid regions. Walking barefoot in contaminated areas can result in infection. Children's sandboxes contaminated with infected feces are also a common source of infection. If you suspect infection, see your physician.

Treatment consists of oral medication repeated in two weeks.

Whipworms—Whipworms are intestinal parasites that are about one quarter inch long. They live in the large intestine and are much more common in dogs than cats. Watery, bloody diarrhea, weight loss, and general debilitation can result from infestation. Eggs are passed in the stool. The eggs are very resistant to drying and heat; they can remain alive in the environment for up to five years. Whipworms pass small numbers of eggs, which means diagnosis can be more difficult and may require examination of multiple stool specimens.

Treatment consists of oral medication which should be repeated in three weeks. Whipworms are not infectious to people.

Coccidia—Coccidia is a single-celled protozoan ingested through dirt or the feces of an infected animal. Isospora and Cryptosporidium species of coccidia most commonly cause clinical symptoms; many cases of coccidia are subclinical, meaning no symptoms are seen. Infected dogs pass immature coccidia in their feces, contaminating the soil, where the oocysts (immature coccidia) can survive for long periods. Infection may occur through ingestion of contaminated soil or ingestion of a mouse infected with coccidia. Coccidia are most dangerous to young animals as the disease may cause severe watery diarrhea, dehydration, abdominal distress, and vomiting.

Treatment consists of oral sulfa-type antibiotics given for 5 to 25 days. In severe infections, it may be necessary to repeat treatment. The most common species of coccidia do not have any effect on humans, however, Cryptosporidium may be transmitted to people. This parasite has also been found in the public water supply of some major cities and poses a health risk for those who are immunocompromised.

Giardia—Giardia is a single-celled parasite that inhabits the intestines of mammals, birds, and amphibians. Mature giardia organisms live in the small intestine where they multiply and become cysts. The cysts are the infective stage and are shed into the feces of the infected animal. They can survive for several weeks in the environment as cysts; when they are eaten by a new host, they repeat the life cycle.

Giardia is spread through feces and contaminated water, soil, or grass. The most common symptom is diarrhea. Giardia can also be spread to humans, although human infection usually occurs secondary to drinking contaminated water. Severe infestations may result in weight loss and dehydration secondary to watery diarrhea. This parasite is easily transmitted between pets within the household.

Treatment consists of oral medication given daily for seven to ten days. Multiple treatments or medications may be needed. All pets in the home should be tested and treated as needed.

Toxoplasmosis—Cats are the primary host for toxoplasma, although the parasite can affect nearly all warm-blooded animals and humans. The main source of transmission is raw meat and unwashed fruits and vegetables. Symptoms of infection can include vomiting, diarrhea, and abdominal pain, but neurological symptoms such as tremors, seizures, uncoordinated gait, muscle weakness, and partial or complete paralysis can also occur. Some cats may only be carriers of the parasites and not show symptoms for a long time or the infection may burst out at any time. Dogs can become infected through ingesting infected soil or cat feces. Cats are infected by eating rodents, contaminated soil, or feces.

The parasite is carried in the blood of the pet; diagnosis is made with a blood test.

Toxoplasma parasites can live for up to one year in the environment. The parasite cannot be destroyed by frost or chemicals; only high heat will kill the parasite.

Humans may get infected with the toxoplasmosis parasite. Healthy humans are immune to the parasite; however, pregnant women should be cautious as the parasite may harm the fetus. Women that have been in contact with the parasite before getting pregnant are not at risk; however, if the contact with the parasite has taken place after the beginning of the pregnancy, the fetus is at risk.

Treatment consists of the antibiotic Clindamycin and anti-protozoan drugs. Treatment may have to be repeated if symptoms recur.

Natural Treatments for Intestinal Parasites

- **Fasting with raw organic apple cider vinegar**: A day of fasting can be highly beneficial for your pet. This is because the body has a greater and better predisposition to detoxifying when it is not exerting energy on digestion. Add two teaspoons of apple cider vinegar into a sixteen-ounce bowl of water. This potent antiseptic will help eliminate the presence of parasites when it passes through the digestive tract.

- **Garlic** is a highly medicinal food since it has potent antibacterial, antifungal, and antiviral properties and is also useful for eliminating intestinal parasites. Contrary to internet lore, garlic is not a forbidden food for dogs and cats. For small dogs, feed up to one quarter clove twice a day, medium dogs half clove twice a day, large dogs three quarters clove twice a day, and giant breeds one clove twice a day. Cats can safely be fed a half clove three times a week. Garlic should be freshly crushed before feeding. A word of caution—do not use garlic for pregnant or lactating animals or animals on blood thinners.

- **Ground pumpkin seeds:** These act as an efficient and smooth laxative. Pumpkin seeds contain an amino acid called cucurbitin. Cucurbitin paralyzes and eliminates the worms from the digestive tract. Grind seeds and give one quarter teaspoon per ten pounds of body weight once or twice a day for one week.

- **Thyme** is a plant with powerful antiseptic activity which will help eliminate the parasites in your pet's gastrointestinal tract. Thyme is especially useful for hookworms. Add one teaspoon per pound of food for several days. Do not use thyme essential oil; use fresh or dried herb. Do not use thyme for pregnant or lactating pets.

- **Dried coconut** can help eliminate worms from the body. Sprinkle unsweetened dried coconut into the food. Guidelines recommend one teaspoon for small dogs, two teaspoons for medium dogs and one tablespoon for large breeds. Coconut oil may also be an effective treatment. Be sure the product used is real coconut, not fake sugary coconut used for baking.

- **Turmeric** is beneficial not only for clearing worms, but also helps repair damage to the intestines due to its anti-inflammatory properties. It can be given as a dried powder or in Golden Paste. The recommended dose is one quarter teaspoon per ten pounds of body weight twice daily. Do not use in pregnant or lactating pets.

- **Chamomile** can be effective against roundworms and whipworms. It works best when given as a tincture. Give one quarter to one half milliliter per twenty pounds body weight twice daily. Do not use if your pet is pregnant or lactating.

- **Pomegranate:** This is especially useful for tapeworms. Add one teaspoon per ten pounds of body weight to your pet's meals twice a day.

Medical Treatments for Intestinal Parasites

Sometimes food alone is not enough to get rid of the worms and you may need medical intervention to solve the problem. Natural treatments can be used in conjunction with medical treatments. Work with your veterinarian to determine the most appropriate treatment plan for your pet. Some of the more common treatments include:

- **Pyrantel pamoate** -This is the active ingredient in Drontal® Plus, PRO-Wormer 2®, Nemex®-2. Side effects include vomiting, depression/lethargy, and anorexia. This drug treats roundworms and hookworms.

- **Fenbendazole**—This is the active ingredient in common

deworming medications including the brand names: Panacur®, Drontal Plus ® and Safe-Guard®. This medication can cause side effects including vomiting, lethargy, anorexia, facial swelling, anaphylaxis, trouble breathing, and collapse. This drug is used to treat roundworms, hookworms, whipworms, and some tapeworms.

🐾 **Praziquantel**—This is the active ingredient in Droncit® and Drontal® Plus (which also includes pyrantel pamoate and fenbendazole). Reported side effects include vomiting, depression/lethargy, diarrhea, and anorexia. This drug is used to treat tapeworms and has recently been added to many monthly heartworm preventative products.

🐾 **Metronidazole**—This drug is used to treat Giardia. Reported side effects include nausea, vomiting, diarrhea, drooling, bloody urine, appetite loss, pancreatitis, liver failure, bone marrow suppression, head tilt, loss of balance, lack of coordination, seizures, and paralysis.

🐾 **Combination Drugs**—Some drug manufacturers combine de-worming ingredients with heartworm drugs. They then market these combinations as preventives for heartworm along with various kinds of intestinal worms. The manufacturers recommend using these drugs monthly. If you use this medication, you are treating your pet unnecessarily for worms he may not have. It is better to have your pet's stool tested twice a year for intestinal parasites; treat only if parasites are present.

All anti-parasitic medications will disrupt the gut microbiome (the good bacteria, fungi, and viruses that are responsible for a healthy immune system). Gut repair with species-appropriate prebiotics and probiotics is crucial after completing medical de-worming procedures.

HEARTWORMS

Heartworm in dogs is a global problem. The domestic dog and wild canids are the main hosts, however, infection in cats and other species has occasionally been reported. All dogs should have a blood test at least once per year for heartworms in areas where heartworms are found.

Transmission

Mosquitoes are the main mode of transmission. The first three stages of larvae develop in mosquitoes. First and second stage larvae require temperatures above 80 F (27 C) for a minimum of two weeks to reach the third stage, which is the infective stage. (This is new, as the old temperature stated was 57 F.) Therefore, transmission may be seasonal in some areas, however, most veterinarians recommend year-round administration of heartworm preventative medications. (I am not one of those veterinarians.)

The infective third stage larvae molt to fourth stage larvae over a couple of weeks in the dog and then mature into the fifth stage, which are immature adults, over a 45- to 60-day period in the muscles. The fifth stage immature adults then enter the bloodstream to be carried to the heart and pulmonary artery where they mature over four to five months. After approximately seven months, the mature adults produce microfilariae that enter the circulation. Because the life cycle takes a long time, diagnosis of heartworm infection is not possible until seven to nine months after the pet is bitten by the infective mosquito.

Prevention

Preventatives such as oral ivermectin and milbemycin oxime, topical moxidectin and selamectin, and injectable, slow release moxidectin kill the L3 and L4 larvae, as well as microfilariae. I do not recommend using moxidectin or selamectin due to the high number of adverse reactions and deaths that have occurred. If I had to choose the least of the evils, milbemycin oxime would be my preferred drug. If you live in an area where heartworms are common but choose not to use preventative medications, it is recommended to test every three to four months so that infection may be caught early before damage is done to the heart and other organs.

It is important to consider the rate of heartworm infection in the area where the dog resides and the lifestyle of the dog. For dogs living outside in hot, humid climates or swampy areas the risk of infection is much higher.

There are no proven natural preventatives, although there is plenty of anecdotal evidence for many herbal products. Repelling mosquitoes by using essential oil sprays made for use on dogs and cats will help. Take pets inside at dusk when the mosquitoes become active.

Diagnosis

Dogs usually show no signs of illness until adult worms are present in the heart. Clinical signs include cough, exercise intolerance, labored respiration, weight loss, fainting, coughing up blood, and congestive heart failure. Interestingly, vomiting is a common sign in cats.

Blood tests are used to detect antigen from female heartworms. False negative test results are possible if there are only male worms present, there is a low number of female worms, or the worms are immature. Blood smears under the microscope may show swimming microfilariae.

Chest X-rays are the best method for determining the severity of disease. Echocardiograms may show worms present in the heart and main pulmonary artery. Laboratory testing may show changes in liver and kidney function.

Treatment

The goal of treatment is to eliminate adult worms, microfilariae, and any migrating third, fourth, and fifth stage larvae. The only FDA approved drug to kill adult worms is Melarsomine Dihydrochloride. Treatment consists of three injections deep into the lumbar (lower back) muscles. One injection is followed by two injections given 24 hours apart one month later. Exercise restriction is essential during this two-month period, as death of the worms can result in pulmonary thromboembolism (blood clots in the lungs).

Steroids are used to help decrease inflammation from worm death and the clinical effects of thromboembolism.

Doxycycline (antibiotic) is used prior to the melarsomine injections. Doxycycline has been shown to kill third and fourth stage larvae. It also kills the *Wolbachia* bacteria found in adult heartworms that help them survive. Heartworm preventative medications as listed above are also started two months prior to melarsomine injections. This is to ensure third and fourth stage larvae will not continue to mature.

Side effects from the injection can include significant irritation at the intramuscular injection sites, accompanied by pain, swelling, tenderness, and reluctance to move. Approximately 30% of treated dogs experience some kind of reaction at the injection site(s). Injection site reactions are generally mild to moderate in severity and recovery occurs in 1 week to 1 month. Firm nodules can persist indefinitely.

Other reactions may include coughing/gagging, depression/lethargy, anorexia/inappetence, fever, lung congestion, coughing up blood, and vomiting. Hypersalivation, vomiting, and panting may occur and may be severe. Death may occur.

An alternative to this "quick kill" method is the "slow kill" method. The slow kill method involves use of Doxycycline for one month, then two months off, then repeat for a period of one year (4 cycles). Monthly preventatives are also given during the year. Most dogs will clear the infection within one year. I have had success with this method with many patients. Traditional veterinarians generally do not like to employ this method. Dogs must lead a sedentary lifestyle until the worms are cleared.

Healthy dogs with a good immune system are less likely to develop overwhelming heartworm infections. It is important to feed a whole-food, human-grade diet. Proper exercise, lean body weight, and immune-support will go a long way to keeping your pet parasite-free.

EXTERNAL PARASITES

Fleas—Fleas are insects that bite dogs and cats to obtain a blood meal. Fleas can transmit tapeworms if eaten by the dog or cat. Fleas found on your pet represent only 5% of the total flea infestation you may be experiencing. There are four stages in the life cycle of fleas: eggs, larvae, pupae, and adults. Carpets and furniture are often overlooked as places where eggs, larvae, and pupae hide out. It is imperative to treat the environment when you experience a flea infestation. Too often chemicals are used repeatedly on the pets while ignoring the environmental load of fleas. This includes treating the yard, as well.

Ticks—Ticks are arachnids (eight-legged like spiders) and are much more difficult to kill than fleas. Ticks can carry diseases such as Lyme, Anaplasmosis, Ehrlichiosis, and Rocky Mounted Spotted Fever, to name a few. Most pet parents are so afraid of their pet contracting one of these diseases that they turn to chemical warfare to prevent ticks from biting their pets. These diseases are treatable. Death from pesticides is not treatable!

Fleas and ticks are carried by wildlife, notably deer, squirrels, and field mice.

Chemicals used to kill fleas and ticks are neurotoxins. While they are meant to kill only the fleas, many pets are also harmed by these drugs. Isoxazoline drugs (Bravecto, Credelio, Nexgard, Simparica, and Revolution Plus are in this category) are labeled with a warning they may be associated with seizures, muscle tremors, and ataxia. This class of drugs was originally researched for their anticoagulant ability in humans. Unfortunately, internal hemorrhage leading to death has also been seen in dogs and cats treated with these products. Other noted side effects include increased thirst and urination, vomiting, diarrhea, anorexia, itching, and skin eruptions. Thousands of dogs and cats have been killed with these products; I do not recommend their use.

Moxidectin is found in topical flea and tick preventatives (Advantage Multi, Advantix, Advocate), as well as injectable heartworm products (Proheart). Neurologic problems and death have also been seen in high numbers with this chemical. Proheart was taken off the market at one time due to the high number of reports of side effects and death. It was brought back on the market years later with no changes to the formulation; instead, a warning label was put on the packaging. Unfortunately, pet owners are not warned about the possible side effects and never see the packaging. The twelve-month Proheart injection contains three times more moxidectin than the injection that lasts for six months. I do not recommend ever using moxidectin in pets.

Chemical collars containing flumethrin and imidacloprid (Seresto) were recently incriminated in causing the deaths of thousands of pets. Since they were introduced in 2012, the Environmental Protection Agency has received over 75,000 incident reports, including nearly 1,000 involving human harm. Side effects include lethargy, anorexia, muscle weakness, tremors, seizures, irritated skin, and death. Other brands of collars use chemicals including amitraz, propoxur, and organophosphates, all of which can cause seizures, weakness, tremors, and death. I do not recommend the use of chemical collars. They are deadly if chewed and can be harmful to children as well.

If your pet has a reaction to any of these chemicals, there is no antidote. Supportive care may include intravenous fluids and hospitalization. Seizures may persist for years, even after the offensive product is no longer given. If your pet has ever been given any of these pesticides, I recommend using a detoxification protocol to help the body heal from the damage they cause.

In my book, *Yin & Yang Nutrition for Dogs*, you can use the Liver Support, Liver Draining, Blood Tonic, and Kidney diets. I also suggest the following supplements for detox of dogs:

- Milk Thistle 50-100 mg per 25 pounds body weight twice daily
- N-acetylcysteine 500 mg twice daily for two weeks, then once daily for two weeks
- Chlorella 25 mg twice daily for three weeks
- The Chinese herb Di Tan Tang for seizures if they are occurring. Give 0.5 gm per 20 pounds body weight twice daily until the pet has been free of seizures for at least three months. This can be given along with traditional anti-seizure medications.
- Liposomal Glutathione 100 mg daily for a week
- Curcumin 100 mg once daily for a week
- Broccoli sprouts 100 mg once daily for a week
- Gaba-aminobutyric acid 100 mg once daily for a week
- Add asparagus and dandelion greens or root to the diet. Dark leafy greens such as kale, beet tops, and spinach may be helpful.

- ☻ Epsom salt/baking soda baths to help pull out toxins
- ☻ MCT oil twice daily, 1 teaspoon per 30 pounds

Some pet parents have continued these supplements for longer periods of time with no adverse effects if the pet is still experiencing symptoms.

I prefer natural prevention for my pets. High quality essential oils made specifically for pets have worked well for my patients in the past. Be careful when applying essential oils; remember that your pet's sense of smell is much stronger than yours. Apply oils in a well-ventilated area and never spray around the pet's face. Do not use oils that are not specifically labeled for use on animals.

Cedar oil has worked well for many of my clients. It is available for use on pets or in the environment. Not everyone likes the smell of cedar; there are many other essential oil products available. Essential oils will also repel mosquitoes. Lavender oil has been shown to repel ticks, while lemongrass oil seems to work particularly well against fleas. Peppermint oil will affect the nervous system of fleas and ticks without harming your pet. Many people use rose geranium oil and find it works well. Neem oil has been around forever and is another favorite. Rose geranium oil is safe to use full strength directly on the pet, but you will only need to apply one drop behind each shoulder blade and one drop near the base of the tail. Other oils should be diluted before applying to pets. Oils can be diluted in extra virgin olive oil or water and rubbed throughout the coat. They can also be diluted by putting a few drops in your favorite pet shampoo or conditioner. A bandanna with a few drops of diluted essential oil can also be used as a natural flea collar. Make sure the smell is not overwhelming, as this will be close to your dog's nose. If using essential oils on cats, be certain they are labeled for use on cats.

Coconut oil kills and repels fleas due to the ingredient lauric acid. Coconut oil can be rubbed through the coat and can be fed to the pets. I use 1 teaspoon per 20 pounds of body weight twice daily in the food. Coconut oil melts at 76 degrees, so rubbing it between your hands will make it into a liquid that you can rub through your pet's coat. It moisturizes skin and helps kill yeast too.

Another great option is garlic for dogs and cats. I have used this in the past in my barn for the horses. We still had flies, but the horses eating it were bothered a lot less than the horses that were not. A lot of people claim dogs and cats will die when fed garlic, but that simply is not true. Fresh crushed garlic can also be added to your pet's diet for flea protection. Anywhere from 1/2 clove to 2 cloves daily would be considered safe, depending on the size of the dog. A good rule of thumb would be no more than 1/2 clove per 20 pounds of body weight daily, with a maximum of 2 cloves for any size dog. Cats can be given ½ a small clove three times a week. However, if you have a pet that has a history of hemolytic anemia, it would be safer to avoid use of garlic in any form.

I do not recommend using Brewer's Yeast tablets for flea prevention. Brewer's yeast basically contains B vitamins, but they are processed and degraded. B vitamins supplied naturally through a healthy diet will be more effective.

Beneficial nematodes can be used to kill flea larvae in your yard. Remember, the squirrels, rabbits, mice, and other small critters outside can be harbingers of fleas. Nematodes will not survive in hot, sunny areas of the lawn, but the fleas and ticks do not like those areas either. So spread these little guys in the shady, moist areas where the fleas and ticks are most likely to be found.

Ticks like cool, shady places, so a short-cut lawn with lots of sun will deter tick infestation. Plant deer-resistant plants in your yard so deer will not be as tempted to enter (I found out the hard way they LOVE tulips!). Plant lavender, sage, mint, wormwood, rosemary, and marigolds, which the fleas and ticks do not like.

If you are in a suitable area, a few chickens (you can collect your own organic eggs!) or guinea hens will go a long way toward keeping tick populations down to a minimum.

Food-grade diatomaceous earth can be sprinkled in the environment or on the pet. Be careful when using it, as you do not want your pet to inhale the dust. DE works by dehydrating the fleas and ticks; it will also be drying to your pet's coat. I prefer to use essential oil sprays made specifically for dogs or cats on the pet and use DE in the environment.

Many people claim vinegar works well. It can be added to the drinking water at the rate of 1 teaspoon per quart of water. We used to make a mixture of white vinegar and Skin So Soft to use on our horses. They had shiny coats and smelled great! Vinegar can also be diluted in water in a 1:1 mixture and sprayed on the coat.

Do not forget the old-fashioned flea comb. The teeth are very close together and will remove fleas and flea eggs. Put the fleas in a bowl of dish soap as you remove them, as this will kill them. These are particularly good for cats because it is a lot harder to bathe a cat. Comb your pets daily if you have any evidence of flea activity.

Vacuum. A lot. Vacuuming will help remove the fleas, eggs, and larvae in the environment. Be sure to get in the corners, under the furniture, and in the crevices under the sofa cushions if your pet sleeps on the furniture. Wash pet bedding often in hot water.

No matter which prevention method you choose, remember that pets can still succumb to diseases spread by these parasites, *even with the use of chemical preventatives.* I have had many patients become ill, even though they had monthly chemicals applied, either topically or orally. Most of the oral and topical products DO NOT REPEL fleas and ticks; they only kill them once they attach to the dog or cat. There are NO guarantees your pet will remain free of pest-borne diseases, no matter what you use.

Keeping your pet free from Lyme disease, Anaplasmosis,

Ehrlichiosis, tapeworms, or other diseases does not mean you need to resort to chemical prevention. Vigilance and common sense, along with the use of natural preventatives, will keep your pets healthier in the long run. Chemicals in topical flea and tick preventatives have been found in waterways and rivers. Our environment is being polluted by the overuse of these products. A study in England revealed that 99% of samples from 20 rivers were polluted with fipronil and imidacloprid. Both were banned for use by farmers for years, but with 10 million dogs and 11 million cats in the UK, with an estimated 80% receiving flea and tick treatments (whether needed or not), the waterways are being polluted. There are currently 66 licensed veterinary products containing fipronil and 21 containing imidacloprid in the UK.

One flea treatment of a medium-sized dog with imidacloprid contains enough pesticide to kill 60 million bees. Dutch research has shown chronic waterway pollution led to sharp drops in insect numbers and falls in bird numbers.

By avoiding the use of chemicals, our environment, and the health of the planet for future generations will be greatly improved.

17

no, no & HECK no!

Ear Cropping, Tail Docking, and Claw Removal

The easiest solution is: Do not do it!

Tail cropping and dewclaw removal are generally performed when puppies are two to five days old. No anesthetic is used during these procedures. Ear cropping is usually performed between eight and twelve weeks of age. This surgery is not to be taken lightly; it must be performed by a veterinarian with the animal under general anesthesia. I have seen many abuse cases where dogs have had ears cropped by breeders or other nonprofessionals using no anesthesia, resulting in infected, mutilated ears. I do not perform ear-cropping and personally think it should be banned.

I used to have Dobermans. My first dog arrived with cropped ears and a docked tail. My second dog had already had his tail docked, but I had to find a veterinarian to crop his ears. The weeks of painful bandage changes that ensued made me vow never to inflict that pain on another dog I owned. From then on, my dogs did not undergo ear cropping procedures and I loved my floppy-eared goofballs. Unfortunately, all my dogs had their tails cropped long before they came to live with me. Until we convince judges and those who set breed standards for the showring that ear cropping and tail docking are cruel, these surgeries will continue to plague certain breeds.

Declaw procedures for cats are generally performed between eight and twenty weeks of age. This procedure must be undertaken only by veterinarians with the kitten under general anesthesia. Very often I see the results of poorly performed declaw surgeries with deformed, painful nails growing back or chronically draining abscesses.

Cats that have been declawed may avoid using the litter box (be sure to use very soft litter instead of large hard granules). They may act painful when jumping down from heights. Since declawed cats have lost one of their defense mechanisms, they are more likely to bite when provoked. Declaw surgeries have been banned in many areas, thankfully.

Full-grown adult cats should not undergo declaw surgery. This procedure is much more painful for adult cats. Insist on a minimum of ten to fourteen days of pain prevention if you choose to have this surgery performed. Cats that have been declawed should never go outside, as they have more difficulty climbing and are less able to defend themselves.

Cats do love to scratch and need an outlet to do so. Scratching posts should be placed throughout your home. They should consist of different surfaces, as each cat will have its own preferences. Include carpet, sisal, corrugated cardboard, and wood surfaces. Teach your cat which areas are appropriate for scratching, and which are off limits (your new leather sofa!). Cardboard boxes are a favorite toy for cats; many will also use them for scratching.

Keep your cat's nails trimmed weekly to decrease damage they might inflict. Nail caps are a great alternative for cats that insist on using your furniture for scratching. Generally, they will remain in place for up to six weeks and are easy to apply using surgical glue. Anti-scratching tapes (basically double-sided adhesive) can be purchased to place on furniture or walls to protect vulnerable surfaces your cat may enjoy scratching.

Before I knew better, all my cats were declawed. For the past twenty years all my cats have retained their nails. They use multiple scratching posts throughout the house. Occasionally they get carried away and use a cloth or leather piece of furniture, but they respond well, abandoning their fun when I make a fuss.

18

Identification

Any animal that goes outside or travels should have identification. Lawn service employees have left my gates open too many times, resulting in dogs running at large. (I have fired quite a few companies for this transgression.) Some of my clients were involved in major traffic accidents resulting in pets running loose—one dog was found two months later thanks to identification tags on the collar. Luckily, the collar stayed in place. I am particularly fond of tags which attach flat on the collar, being nearly impossible to dislodge. They also do not make noise if the animal scratches or shakes its head. Another option is an embroidered collar that has a phone number for contact information.

New technology provides tags with QR codes that can be read by smartphones. The tag is attached to the collar. This is great provided the pet does not lose the collar and the owner has kept the database up to date. Global Positioning System trackers are also available to track your pet.

Collars are more problematic for cats, especially cats that go outside. One client found her cat hanging from his collar in a soccer goal net in her neighbor's yard, unable to get free. One of my cats managed to get his hanging collar tag lodged in a floor heat vent and was stuck sitting in that position until I found him when I came home from work (this can happen to dogs as well with hanging collar tags).

Other forms of identification include tattoos and microchips. When I was first in practice, we tattooed driver's license information on the dog's abdomen at the time of spay or neuter. Looking back, I think that is a terrible way to identify a pet. The number is long, subject to change, and hard to track down. Some breeds come with ear or abdominal tattoos performed by the breeder, which is fine if someone finding the pet knows where to find information leading to the owner. The National Dog Registry is the largest database for pet tattoos in the United States.

Microchips are made by multiple companies. Microchips are the size of a piece of rice; they sit within bioglass and contain essential information about your pet. Microchips are implanted between the pet's shoulder blades using a large-bore needle, however they can migrate throughout the body. When the procedure is done, the information on the chip is sent to a national registry. It is imperative to keep the information up to date; changes in address or phone number must be submitted to the registry database. Not all microchips are read with one scanning device. Some microchips are only compatible with scanners of the same manufacturer. I rarely see problems resulting from microchip implantation, but I have had two patients develop reactions around the chip, resulting in chip removal.

19

Spay or Neuter

Before I became involved with holistic medicine, I would have said that all pets should be spayed or neutered at six months of age before the females have their first heat cycle. This is a popularly held belief in the United States; however, in some European and Asian nations, it is a very unpopular notion. The single biggest reason to spay or neuter is population control. Thousands and thousands of animals are euthanized at shelters every year due to unwanted production of puppies and kittens. However, if we could all be responsible pet owners and keep our young pets from being accidentally bred, I feel our pets would be healthier by allowing them to at least reach full maturity before considering spay or neuter.

I do not support pediatric spay and neuter, but I do understand the usefulness when adoption agencies and shelters want to get puppies and kittens adopted and know they will not be able to breed. Our local shelter tried for years to use prepaid vouchers for spay and neuter of young animals when they reached six months of age after adoption. Sadly, in retrospective analysis they found that a mere 33% of adoptive owners presented the adopted animals for spay or neuter, even though they had already paid for the surgery.

Many shelters are spaying and neutering by eight weeks of age. There have been many studies showing long term health problems related to early spay/neuter. When pets are spayed or neutered, the ovaries and testicles are removed, thereby removing most of the sex hormones produced by the body.

Obesity, some cancers, behavior disorders, hypothyroidism, Cushing's disease and other endocrine diseases, musculoskeletal disorders such as hip and elbow dysplasia, incontinence, and urinary tract infections may occur more frequently in pets undergoing early spay or neuter. A study on Rottweilers showed dogs spayed or neutered before one year of age had a one-in-four lifetime risk of bone cancer and the de-sexed animals were significantly more likely to develop the disease than intact dogs of the same breed.

Spaying or neutering dogs or cats prior to closure of the growth plates causes the growth plates to remain open longer, allowing the long bones to grow longer. The increased length of the femur in the hind legs and radius/ulna in the front legs can push the bones out of the hip and elbow sockets, respectively, resulting in dysplasia and arthritis. Studies have also shown a higher incidence of cruciate ligament tears in dogs that have been de-sexed.

Recent retrospective studies have shown higher incidence of some cancers in dogs that have undergone spay or neuter prior to maturation. Hemangiosarcoma of the spleen or heart, osteosarcoma of the bones, prostate cancer, mast cell cancer, lymphoma, brain tumors, and lower urinary tract cancers have a higher incidence of occurrence in animals spayed or neutered early. The estrogen and testosterone hormones seem to have some protective effects.

On the other hand, mammary cancer may increase in un-spayed older females, although a 2012 study in the United Kingdom Journal of Small Animal Practice concluded there was not enough evidence to support that theory. Ovarian cancer and malignant testicular cancer are not very common in dogs and cats but may occur if the gonads are left in place. The incidence of uterine infection or pyometra, which is life threatening, increases with age.

Cats are not small dogs—malignant mammary cancer in cats is a much bigger problem. Cats should be spayed by one year of age to reduce risks of mammary cancer and pyometra. Male cats are generally neutered by one year of age to reduce urine spraying and aggression toward other cats. Neutering will decrease urine odor as well. Male cats should be allowed to develop to full maturity (nine to twelve months of age) prior to neutering to allow full development of the urethra, with hopes of decreasing risk of urinary blockage, although there is little scientific evidence to back this up.

Currently, I think allowing female dogs to undergo two or three heat cycles and to develop to maturity is the best answer. Many of my clients are leaving male dogs intact for life. Sterilization without removal of the gonads (ovaries and testes) may be a good solution. This includes ovary-sparing-spay, tubal ligation, and vasectomy. Although these techniques in animals are not commonly used, there does seem to be some movement toward using these procedures. For more information about these alternative options, visit https://www.parsemus.org/ Again, being a responsible pet owner and not allowing a pet to be accidentally bred is paramount.

Studies of intact males, particularly large breed dogs, have shown there may be beneficial protection against cancers such as prostate cancer, hemangiosarcoma, and osteosarcoma. Testicular cancers can occur but have a low mortality rate. Benign prostatic enlargement is common in older unneutered males but is usually treatable. Prostate cancer occurrence is much higher in neutered male dogs and is difficult to treat. Perineal and inguinal hernias occur much more commonly in unneutered males than neutered males and these can be life-threatening if the bladder becomes entrapped in the hernia.

Neutering males can help decrease unwanted behaviors such as aggression, urine marking, and desire to roam. However, some studies have shown increased aggression after neutering. Proper training can solve most of those issues. In my opinion, male dogs should be left intact when possible due to the number of health problems associated with neutering.

The one contradiction is the case of a retained testicle which has not descended into the scrotum. Retained testicles have a very high rate of developing into cancerous tumors as the temperature inside the body is higher than the temperature in the scrotum. Retained testicles should always be removed if they have not descended into the scrotum by one year of age. Some acupuncturists have had success in getting the testicles to descend using herbal treatment such as epimedium along with acupuncture.

20

Choosing the Right Diet for Your Pet

This is one of the hardest decisions facing pet owners. I am asked every day which foods I recommend. Having your pet live for two to three decades will require high quality nutrition to support their overall health. Just walking through the grocery store pet food aisle or walking into a pet food store will make your head spin with the endless variety of choices. Pet *feed* manufacturers use many tricks to put a positive spin on poor quality food. Sadly, it is up to the consumer to understand what is really in the food because the pet feed industry is not as well-regulated as you are led to believe.

Over the years, I have become less satisfied with commercial pet food products. My distrust of the big pet food companies has escalated with the number of recalls and deaths of beloved pets dying when fed tainted pet foods. Pet feed has been recalled for con-tamination with salmonella, listeria, aflatoxins, molds, melamine, euthanasia solution, excess vitamins and minerals, and deficiencies of vitamins and minerals.

The feeding of home-prepared food has become very popular with pet owners; a large contingency now gravitates to feeding raw diets. Vitamin and mineral deficiencies can be common in improperly prepared diets. For those wanting to prepare their own pet food, there are many balanced recipes available and there are supplements made specifically to help balance home-prepared meals. I have an online course *Home-Made Food for Dogs 101*, as well as my book *Yin & Yang Nutrition for Dogs: Maximizing Health with Whole Foods, Not Drugs,* which you can use to learn to prepare meals at home.

I resisted feeding raw meats to my pets for years, believing all the scare tactics about bacterial contamination and illnesses in pets and people. But once I started feeding commercial raw foods to my pets, I saw big differences in their mobility, coat, disappearance of skin and ear infections and improved overall health. For those new to raw feeding, it is best to find a reputable company using ingredients sourced from countries known to produce clean meats. Once you are comfortable feeding raw products, you may want to venture into making your own complete raw food diets. Be sure to educate yourself on nutritional guidelines before making your own pet food.

Many holistic and open-minded veterinarians are starting to push for raw feeding. The old-school veterinarians still abhor raw feeding; the American Animal Hospital Association and the American Veterinary Medical Association both have a policy against raw feeding. The Centers for Disease Control provided a statement to the American Veterinary Medical Association rec-ommending against feeding raw food to dogs and cats because of the risk of illness to the pet as well as to people living in the household, going so far as to state **"Do not feed your pet a raw diet."** (Bold emphasis is theirs, not mine.) The American Animal Hospital Association approved their policy in August 2012 which discourages feeding raw meat to pets. This policy was supported by the National Association of State Public Health Veterinarians and the American Association of Feline Practitioners. These are harsh statements.

When reading the CDC website discussing these statements, they also say that to date, there have been NO reports of human illness associated with raw food diets. However, in 2006 to 2008 there was a multistate outbreak of Salmonella infections in 79 people traced back to dry dog food. And in 2012, another 49 people were infected with Salmonella from dry dog food. According to Dr. Conor Brady, in his book *Feeding Dogs: Dry or Raw? The Science Behind the Debate*, from 2012 to 2019, 68,000 tons of dry food have been recalled for pathogenic bacteria. During the same time, only 900 tons of raw were recalled for the same issue." There are documented outbreaks of Salmonella in people from processed pet treats such as pig ears, rawhides, and cow hooves. Personally, I do not understand the negativity about raw feeding when the data point solidly toward processed foods causing more human illness than feeding raw products to pets.

Recently, more companies are using human grade and organic ingredients, which is exactly what your pet should be eating. Pet feed made with ingredients that are not human grade can include diseased meats that are classified as inedible. While diseased or decaying meat is technically not allowed in pet food, the FDA refuses to enforce this law. Rendered ingredients in pet food are commonly sourced from animals that were dead but were not slaughtered for food purposes.

For those who worry about feeding a raw food product, there

are quite a few companies offering gently cooked, human-grade food choices. This is a great way to provide wholesome nutrition without having to formulate and prepare the meals yourself. If you can read and pronounce all the listed ingredients and the food looks like real food that you recognize, you know you have found a winner! The company should be able to provide you with a detailed analysis of the vitamin and mineral content in the formulation, showing that it is a complete and balanced diet suitable for long-term feeding.

Dry kibble pet food is the most common formulation fed to pets today. It is convenient and easy to feed, easy to store, and is usually palatable to most pets. Dry food has a long shelf life, but that can have its own problems. Dry food may be stored on the shelf at the manufacturing plant for a few months, then shipped and stored at the sales location for a few more months, and then stored at your house for months depending on how quickly you use the product. Most expiration dates on bags of dry food are at least one year out from the manufacturing date, sometimes more. It would be more useful for the consumer if the pet food manufacturing company put the manufacturing date on the bag so consumers would be sure they were buying fresh product.

One of the biggest problems with dry food that has been stored for long periods of time is storage mites. Over 80% of dry food stored for more than a few months will test positive for storage mites. Storage mites are a common cause of skin allergies and itching in dogs and cats. If you feel you absolutely must feed dry food to your pets, please buy a small bag that you will use completely within one month. Store the food in the original bag in an airtight container. The bag has a coated lining to help keep the food from becoming rancid. Dry kibble is sprayed with fats and Animal Digest (a slurry made from enzymatic or *chemical* hydrolysis of rendered animals and animal parts) to improve palatability, but those fats become rancid when exposed to heat, light, and air.

Always keep the label from the bag. That way you will have a list of ingredients and the lot number and expiration date in case there is a recall. Recalls can be found on the FDA website or at www.truthaboutpetfood.com.

I have many reasons why I do not recommend kibble-based diets for dogs and cats.

Dogs and cats were originally designed to hunt and eat wild prey. Wild prey contains a very high moisture content, generally 65 to 70%. Most raw diets and canned food diets will fall somewhere in the 65 to 75% moisture range, whereas dry kibble generally contains only 6 to 10% moisture.

Moisture is needed for food to be digested, so where does the pet get the moisture for digestion if it is not in the food? The answer: the moisture is transported from the cells of the body into the digestive tract. The chronic drain of fluid from the body causes stress to the organs, particularly the kidneys. Kidneys need moisture to maintain optimal function. Pets consuming dry diets generally remain in a state of low-grade dehydration. Over a lifetime, this leads to a deficiency of moisture in the body. Pets that are moisture-deficient may have dry coats, dry foot pads, a dry and cracked nose, flaky skin, a dark pink or red tongue, and excessive panting.

Lipomas, which are large, fatty deposit lumps under the skin, are more commonly found in dogs fed dry food. They can form anywhere on the body, but are commonly seen under the neck and armpits, along the lower sides and underneath the chest and abdomen, into the groin area. Almost all lipomas are benign, but cancerous liposarcomas can occur. I used to raise Dobermans before changing to Cavalier King Charles Spaniels. When I fed dry food, my dogs had dozens of lipomas. Once I switched to raw feeding, my dogs no longer suffered with these masses.

Some people soak kibble in water before feeding, thinking this will replace the moisture that is lacking. However, to get the kibble back to the level of moisture found in whole prey, over 4 cups of water would need to be added to each cup of dry food. Depending on the quality of the kibble, it may or may not actually soak up the water.

Some kibble remains hard, even after sitting in water for hours. (Test your kibble by adding water and letting the bowl sit.) That hard kibble is not very digestible. Stomach acid will help break it down, depending how long the kibble sits in the stomach. But have you ever seen a pet vomit partially digested food where the kibble comes up whole? This is a common occurrence, particularly with cats.

On the other hand, kibble that blows apart and makes a very large volume when water is added can be dangerous for animals prone to bloat. This is one of the reasons owners of large breed dogs will break the meals into several feedings, to avoid production of gas when the kibble swells in the stomach and intestines. Increased plant fiber in kibble slows the passage of digesta through the intestines, resulting in increased gas production, which can lead to bloat.

Most pets fed dry kibble will drink more than pets that eat high moisture food. Many clients tell me their pets stop, or considerably decrease, water intake when the diet is changed away from kibble.

Unfortunately, cats are not big water drinkers. Their ancestors were desert dwellers and relied on the moisture in their diet for survival. They like their water served fresh, which is why many will only drink from a dripping faucet or immediately after fresh water is placed in the bowl. Cats are extremely sensitive to the smell of bacteria and will shy away from stale water that might be contaminated. They also do not like their water served next to their food, so place the water bowl in a different area. Because cats are not big drinkers, they will make very concentrated urine when they are fed dry food.

In both dogs and cats, the more concentrated the urine, the higher chance of having crystals form in the urine. Crystals cause pain and bleeding in the bladder and can progress to stone formation and urinary obstruction. Higher moisture content in the diet will result in more dilution of the urine. More frequent flushing of the bladder with dilute urine decreases the possibility of stone formation and obstruction. Cats should not be fed dry food, as they are prone to obesity and diabetes from carbohydrates, as well as urinary and kidney disease from lack of moisture.

Many dry cat food products have dl-methionine added to lower the pH of the urine to decrease production of crystals and stones in the urine. This additive is synthetically made from petroleum derivatives. Added dl-methionine indicates a diet is high in starches and carbohydrates, but low in meat content, as meat is already high in naturally occurring methionine. Feeding a healthy, high-moisture, high-meat diet will automatically decrease production of urinary crystals.

Any pets that have a history of kidney or bladder stone formation should not be fed kibble. Even the prescription diet kibbles make no sense. These pets need moisture. The prescription diets have added salt to make the pets drink more and chemicals to change the pH of the urine. Why not feed a species-appropriate, high-moisture diet instead?

Feeding a bowl of dry kibble is like eating a bowl of dry cereal. How would your body feel if the only thing you ever consumed was dry cereal that had a synthetic vitamin/mineral mix added in? While that might be considered a complete diet containing all the vitamins and minerals needed for survival, it most certainly would not result in vibrant health. Yet this is exactly what the majority of the population is feeding their pets, as recommended by their veterinarians!

How many times have you heard you should shop the outside perimeter of the grocery store? That is where they keep all the fresh fruits, meats, and vegetables. All the center aisles contain the processed foods that are less nutritious. Where is dry kibble found in the food store? YES—in the processed food aisles.

Kibble is made by processing food at high heat, usually being cooked four to five times. Poultry meals (turkey meal, chicken meal, etc.) are made by grinding the entire bird, including feathers and feces. It sounds gross because it is. Of course, kibble is not supposed to be contaminated with fecal bacteria, so the ground poultry bodies (along with roadkill, dead zoo animals, and other unsavory meats) are cooked at high heat to kill bacteria. After cooking to make a pot of disgusting soup, the soup is dehydrated using heat, to make a powdered meal. The meal is shipped to the pet food manufacturer where it will be combined with the cooked grains and other ingredients, then cooked again to make a dough. The dough is cooked under high heat and pushed through an extruder (shaping die) and cut into kibble sized pieces. Then it is dried again to remove enough moisture to give it a stable shelf life. After this process, it is sprayed with fats to increase palatability.

Shelf life is great, but how much "life" is left in the food? Because the amino acids, essential fatty acids, and vitamins have been destroyed by cooking, the pet food manufacturers will "fortify" the food with an added vitamin/mineral mix. This mix is usually synthetic and is often imported from overseas. Occasionally excesses of vitamins or minerals are added, resulting in product recalls if enough pets are made ill by the product.

Greg Alldrich, PhD is a consultant to the pet food industry. He states that "*extensive processing can increase variability,* destroy essential nutrients and create unwholesome by-products. *From a formulator's perspective, this creates a dilemma regarding how to assure the diet is sufficiently fortified while avoiding excess after accounting for processing effects.*"

In other words, they really do not know how much nutrition remains in the food or how much of each vitamin and mineral needs to be added after processing. Unless each batch is tested after all the processing, there is no way to know. Many pets were killed recently when that vitamin/mineral mix contained excess levels of vitamin D which caused kidney failure.

We are dealing with a pet food industry that lies and hides the truth about ingredients they use. Consumers buy high-priced kibble, thinking they are providing their pets with the best possible diet. The truth is that many ingredients are waste products from the human food industry including inedible meats derived from sick livestock. The pet food companies put pictures of steak and fresh vegetables on the bag labels, wanting you to believe their food is the same that you put on your own table to serve your family. Other companies want you to believe your dogs and cats are being fed like wolves and lions in the wild, just as nature intended. I am certain that wolves and lions in the wild are not eating dehydrated food that has been cooked at high temperatures until it has minimal nutritional value.

If you love your pets as much as I love mine, you will think long and hard about the diet you feed. Our pets give us unconditional love and they deserve the best. I realize the pet food market has misleading advertising and there is a confusing debate about what is best to feed. The ideal food will vary with every pet and there is no "one size fits all". Do your research. Ask questions. Avoid a kibble-based diet. At the very least, add fresh food toppers to the kibble to enhance nutrient value.

Be aware that packaging may state "made in the USA" yet ingredients may be sourced from elsewhere. Look for labels that state "sourced in the USA" if that is your country of choice. Many good products also originate in the UK, New Zealand, Australia, France, and Canada.

To choose the right pet food, you must be able to read the labels on the bags and cans of food that you buy. Ingredients are listed on the label in decreasing quantities, meaning the first ingredient listed is found in the highest quantity. Cats are obligate carnivores, which means they need to eat meat. Dogs are either carnivores or omnivores, depending on who you ask, but they definitely lean to a more carnivorous dietary history. Either way, they should all be eating a meat-based diet. So, it stands to reason the main ingredients in their foods should be meat. If you read a food label and the first ingredient is not meat, do not buy the food.

I do have some vegan clients who will not feed meat to their pets. Dogs can adapt to a vegan diet (although it is not ideal). In my opinion, cats should never be fed a vegetarian or vegan diet. I have lost many feline patients to heart disease and overwhelming infections because their owners refused to feed meat. No matter how many vitamins you add to the diet, you still cannot achieve the amino acid and vitamin profile that an obligate carnivore needs for ideal health without feeding meat, in my opinion.

The first ingredient should be a whole meat source. If you absolutely feel you must feed kibble to your pet, I recommend that the first two, preferably three ingredients to be meat or organs. When adding up the percentages of the first five ingredients listed, remember that three grains or vegetables will outweigh two meats, so you will be feeding a high-carbohydrate product. Dry kibble is loaded with carbohydrates to make the kibble stick together. The maximum amount of meat that can be included in a dry kibble food is around 30%. (Do not confuse this with air-dried meat products that have the appearance and texture of a dry food.)

Beware of "ingredient splitting"—a trick used by pet food manufacturers to decrease the amount of meat in a product but make it look like there is more meat than vegetable. Peas may be listed as whole peas, pea starch, pea fiber, pea protein, and pea flour. That is a lot of peas!

Ingredients such as Animal Digest, Animal Fat, Dried Egg Product, Meat and Bone Meal, Beef Tallow, generic Fish Meal, Fish Oil, or By-Product Meal will not appear on the label of a good quality food. FDA studies have found detectable levels of euthanasia solution in meat and bone meal, beef and bone meal, animal digest, and animal fat, meaning euthanized animals were used to make the product. Pets fed these ingredients are consuming euthanasia solution daily. Bone meal is a poor-quality product used to increase the protein content in foods. "Animal fat" is sometimes added as a cheap, unspecified fat source, and can contain high quantities of chemicals that can be found in diseased animals. Ol' Roy, Pedigree, Big Heart Pet brands, Kibbles N Bits, Purina, Beneful, Chef Michael, Cesar, Alpo, Whiskas, and Special Kitty are some of the foods that use these ingredients.

I recommend avoiding wheat in any form, white rice, brewer's rice (which is a cheap, non-nutritive filler), brewer's yeast extract, corn in any form, dried beet pulp, rice hulls, ground psyllium husks, or soy in the food. These are less expensive fillers used to increase the protein level in the food. Many pets have allergies to these grains and fillers.

Avoid any kind of glutens added to a diet. Commonly, wheat, corn, or rice glutens are used as a binder in canned foods. Sugar and high fructose corn syrup are added to improve taste and pre-serve the food. These have no place in pet food. Dyes are added to color the bits of food to make them more pleasing to the eye of the consumer (not the pet—they really do not care about the color of the food). Some of these dyes have been incriminated as causing cancer and Attention-Deficit/Hyperactivity Disorder in children.

Preservatives such as Ethoxyquin, Glyceryl Monostearate, BHA,

BHT, and propylene glycol have been linked to cancers and illness in pets and people. Pet food manufacturers do not have to list Ethoxyquin on the label if it was added to preserve meat or fish meal by another company before being sent to the manufacturer of the final food product. Fish meal is the product most likely to be preserved using these chemicals. Many of these preservatives have been outlawed in the human food industry yet are still allowed to be used to poison our pets.

I prefer to buy food from companies that own their own processing facilities. Companies may outsource to a food processing facility, which may substitute lower quality products that can be purchased more cheaply. When a contaminated grain or meat product is used in one of the processing facilities, many brands of pet food will be recalled because they were all processed in the same plant. The FDA maintains a website that shows pet food recalls. I recommend looking at the site occasionally to see which brands have been recalled. There are quite a few repeat offenders on the list.

The other thing to consider when choosing the right product to feed your pets is the form in which the food will be fed; canned, dry, raw, or home-cooked. The worst form is the packaged plastic pouches containing semi-moist food. Ingredients for one of the more popular semi-moist foods include: beef by-product, soy grits, soy flour, high fructose corn syrup, wheat flour, corn syrup, animal fat, yellow 6, red 40, yellow 5, and Ethoxyquin. That is a whole list of things I just listed should never be found in pet food! When I tried to look up the ingredients in semi-moist foods I had to go to the store and read the package label. The ingredients are so awful they are not listed on the company website. I have seen many pets with chronic skin disease, allergies, cancer, and diabetes that have been fed these semi-moist products for long periods of time.

I do not recommend prescription veterinary diets because I feel many companies use low-quality ingredients to formulate the diets. I do appreciate that the prescription diet companies spend a lot of money on research and support of the veterinary community, but I cannot support the use of poor-quality ingredients. The first five ingredients in one dry feline prescription diet include: corn gluten meal, animal fat, whole grain corn, soybean mill run, and dried egg product. Every one of those ingredients is on our do-not-feed list! This is a partial list of ingredients for a canned canine prescription diet: water, corn flour, pork liver, rice flour, beef by-products, dried beet pulp. Awful!

In summary when shopping for pet food:

- Look for high quality meat proteins
- Look for human-grade ingredients
- Avoid meat by-products
- Avoid Animal Digest, Animal Fat, Meat and Bone Meal
- Avoid preservatives such as BHA, BHT, Ethoxyquin, Glycerol Monostearate, and Propylene Glycol
- Avoid corn, wheat, brewer's rice, soy, rice hulls, and dried beet pulp
- Avoid wheat gluten, corn gluten, and rice gluten or gluten meals
- Avoid dyes and colorings
- Avoid sugar and high fructose corn syrup
- Avoid all semi-moist foods in cellophane pouches

The second most fed form of pet food is a canned diet. Canned food is cooked and processed at lower heat than dry food, so it retains more of the vitamins that naturally occur in the food. It has a long shelf life, usually for years; however, it would be nice to know the manufacturing date.

Canned food has a high moisture content, which is much healthier, and therefore makes it preferable over dry food. Most pets love canned foods and will eat them readily. However, when choosing a canned food, you, as the consumer, should be very picky! Most canned foods will contain some sort of binder or gluten. The glutens are usually corn, rice, or wheat. Other binders commonly used are guar gum and carrageenan. Buy foods without these additives which can be highly inflammatory, contributing to inflammatory bowel disease and allergies. Binders such as porcine plasma or montmorillonite clay are much better.

If you choose to buy canned food, be sure to look at the cost per pound. Many small cans look attractively priced, until you figure out you are paying seven to ten dollars per pound. You could feed your pet steak for less.

For more information regarding high-quality diets, visit www.truthaboutpetfood.com. Susan Thixton does research on pet food companies annually and publishes "The List" of pet foods she would be willing to feed her own dogs and cats. All companies must provide verification to human grade ingredients and meats sourced from humanely raised animals. I have a shorter list on my website, www.drjudymorgan.com, which can be obtained by signing up for our weekly newsletter.

The DCM (Dilated Cardiomyopathy) Debacle

In recent years, some veterinarians have blamed grain-free, boutique pet foods for causing a heart disease known as Dilated Cardiomyopathy. Unfortunately, the FDA investigation has not been updated since June 2019—over two years with no answers.

The veterinary community has bought into this rhetoric, often recommending a return to poor quality, grain-filled, low-meat diets for dogs and cats. Pet food consumers who have been buying higher priced, higher quality foods are now being told to return to cheap, low-quality diets that, in my opinion, do not provide the optimal nutrition our pets need.

Up to 75% of all cardiovascular disease in dogs is chronic degenerative valve disease. The second most common heart disease is reported to be DCM or Dilated Cardiomyopathy. This is a condition in which the heart muscle becomes thin and ineffective at pumping blood, resulting in a very enlarged or dilated heart. Historically, DCM has been considered primarily an inherited disease, found commonly in breeds such as Great Danes, Dobermans, Boxers, Irish Wolfhounds, Cocker Spaniels, and Newfoundlands (and now Golden Retrievers).

Symptoms include panting, lethargy, coughing, lack of appetite, bloated abdomen, and collapse. Diagnosis is made using electrocardiograms, radiographs, and echocardiography.

In the past few years, concerns have been raised by veterinary cardiologists and nutritionists that more cases of DCM have been diagnosed than normal. Questions were raised regarding the relationship of diets such as grain-free diets, legume-filled diets, novel protein diets, and diets produced by small manufacturers with the uptick in cases of DCM. Although there was no proof that these diets cause cardiomyopathy, some individuals (mostly funded by large pet food companies) were very outspoken about the need to move away from these diets and return to feeding grain-filled kibble manufactured by major pet food corporations.

Doctors at veterinary colleges have been very outspoken on this matter; however, their opinions may be swayed by the funding they receive. "Dr. Freeman has received research support from, given sponsored lectures for, or provided professional services to Aratana Therapeutics, Hill's Pet Nutrition, Nestlé Purina PetCare, and Royal Canin. Dr. Heinze has done consulting for Lafeber and WellPet, given sponsored talks for Nestlé Purina PetCare and the Pet Food Institute; and provided professional services to Balance IT.com and Mark Morris Institute. Dr. Linder has received speaker fees or research funding from Hill's Pet Nutrition, Nestlé

Purina PetCare, and Royal Canin, and has provided professional services for Mark Morris Institute." -Tufts Petfoodology

These doctors have been recommending that pet owners feed only foods made by the big pet food companies: Purina, Hill's, Royal Canin...conflict of interest, perhaps?

A review of veterinary teaching hospital records showed an incidence of DCM of 0.4% of the dogs seen. Based on an estimated population of 77,000,000 dogs in the United States, we would expect over 300,000 dogs to be diagnosed with DCM at this incidence rate. Yet the FDA released a public statement incriminating pet food based on a mere 560 cases. There was no science or research to back their statement.

Taurine is an amino acid found in meat and is required for heart muscle function. Dogs and cats need taurine in their diet. Dogs can make taurine from amino-acid precursors (methionine and cysteine), whereas cats do not perform this metabolism very efficiently. Because of this, feline diets have been supplemented with taurine for decades. Prior to the addition of taurine to cat food, many cats were diagnosed with dilated cardiomyopathy secondary to taurine deficiency.

We do know that diets low in protein, taurine, and sulfur-containing amino acids methionine and cysteine (such as prescription diets designed to manage urate stones) HAVE been associated with taurine-deficient DCM. When these diets are supplemented with taurine and L-carnitine (another amino acid critical for heart function), DCM clinical signs can be reversed.

The number of Golden Retrievers with DCM has been increasing, raising the question of a genetic propensity toward disease. Recent studies have noted Golden Retrievers may be at risk for developing DCM but have failed to identify a definitive causal relationship between diet, taurine, and cardiac function. Differences in measuring taurine concentration also play a role: the relationship between whole blood taurine, plasma taurine, and cardiac muscle taurine concentrations remains unknown.

Many nutrients other than taurine are important for ideal heart health including carnitine, thiamin, copper, vitamin E, selenium, magnesium, choline, and potassium. Faults can be found within DCM studies in dogs including sampling bias, inconsistencies in sampling parameters, too many variables, and lack of complete data for case studies on DCM and known genetic predisposition in certain dog breeds. Small sample sizes and overrepresentation of breeds are commonplace in recent DCM studies. Studies involving multiple breeds and larger sample groups are warranted to better understand if relationships exist between potential causes (such as diet) and the development of DCM for the overall dog population.

On June 27, 2019, the FDA released an updated list of dogs affected by DCM. Of the 305 dogs listed, 73% were breeds with known genetic predisposition for DCM. Also, 61% of the dogs included had other diseases which may have contributed to cardiac disease, including hypothyroidism, Lyme disease, and mitral valve degeneration. It is impossible to implicate specific types of dog food as being a causative factor when the data is already skewed.

Boutique diets, defined as produced by a small manufacturer, have been implicated in association with DCM. However, when the FDA report is broken down into which pet food manufacturers made the called-out diets, 49% of the brands listed were made by one of the six largest pet food manufacturers in North America. Given that almost half of the brands listed on the FDA report on June 27, 2019, are not manufactured by boutique pet food companies, it is unlikely that an association can be made to DCM. This did not stop veterinarians or the FDA from incriminating smaller pet food manufacturers, resulting in huge losses in revenue and jobs for many of those companies. Seventy-six percent of the proteins listed in the FDA report included chicken, beef, pork, lamb, salmon, turkey, and whitefish, which are NOT exotic proteins that the FDA labeled as problematic.

A study performed at the University of Illinois in which dogs were fed a diet with 45% legumes (peas, lentils) showed no differences in plasma amino acids (taurine, carnitine) from dogs fed diets without legumes. Although the FDA has called-out grain-free diets and implicated legumes as causative agents of DCM, this study shows no relation.

In December 2022, FDA ended their "study" on DCM related to grain-free diets. The agency stated based on the reports of DCM cases received, "they do not supply sufficient data to establish a causal relationship with reported product(s)" and they do not intend to release any further information about the issue "until there is meaningful new scientific information to share". In other words, the FDA does not believe grain-free pet foods are/were the cause of DCM in dogs, even though the original announcement resulted in significant loss of revenue for many pet food manufacturers and thousands of dogs and cats were switched to poor-quality foods containing grains due to their original report. Sadly, many veterinarians have jumped on the DCM bandwagon, insisting that pets be fed dry kibble formulated with grains which is exactly the opposite of what our pets should be eating.

Many pet owners have been made to feel guilty for feeding what they considered to be higher-quality diets. Unfortunately, there is no basis for this. The pet food and veterinary communities rushed to a conclusion that has no support. Our pets need MEAT in their diets to maintain good health.

I do not recommend feeding kibble-based diets to our pets. If you avoid feeding a diet that consists mainly of carbohydrate-laden kibble, it is easy to provide enough meat to satisfy the requirements for taurine in the diet. Cats and dogs are not designed to thrive on grains, legumes, potatoes, and starches. Provide diets with high meat content to ensure good health. My dogs are never fed starchy ingredients. Their diet consists of 80% meat, organs, and bone (they are raw fed), and 20% non-starchy vegetable matter. Most of our dogs live well into their late teens.

HOMEMADE PUPLOAF

Years ago, I created a recipe called Puploaf. It became an internet sensation; I was amazed how many dog owners were looking for a balanced recipe they could make at home. There have been many versions published and the recipe can be varied if your dog has an allergy to any of the ingredients. I do not recommend feeding this for puppies under six months of age, particularly for large breeds, as the calcium to phosphorus balance must be carefully managed during growth. Pre-made Puploaf is available for purchase in the United States through www.AllProvide.com.

- ☐ 1 pound 90% lean ground beef
- ☐ 4 ounces ground beef heart
- ☐ 3 ounces ground beef liver
- ☐ 8 ounces ground chicken or turkey gizzards
- ☐ 2 eggs ground with shell
- ☐ 4 ounces ground butternut squash
- ☐ 6 ounces ground vegetables including kale, spinach, broccoli, green beans, red pepper
- ☐ 3 ounces ground Shiitake mushrooms
- ☐ 2 ounces cranberries

- ☐ 1 teaspoon ground fresh ginger
- ☐ 1 tablespoon flax seed oil
- ☐ 1 teaspoon kelp or 2 ounces of mussels
- ☐ 1 teaspoon sea salt
- ☐ 2 sardines, canned in water, should be added at the time of feeding (1/2 to 1 for small dogs). They can be added during cooking, but they smell bad.

Mix all ingredients together. May be fed raw or baked at 325 F for 30 to 45 minutes, depending on thickness and size of pan; should be lightly done, not over-cooked (juicy in the center). If your pet has a beef or chicken allergy, turkey or lean ground pork could be substituted.

Feed 2 to 3% of body weight daily (for instance, a 50-pound dog would eat 1 to 1.5 pounds per day). Food should be fed warm, not cold from the refrigerator.

Freeze any portion that will not be used within five days.

For more home-prepared diets, there are many recipe books available, some better than others. I have written a few recipe books for dogs; I would recommend *Yin & Yang Nutrition for Dogs: Maximizing Health with Whole Foods, Not Drugs* as the most informative.

HOMEMADE CATLOAF

Catloaf is a newer recipe designed specifically for cats. Cats are very finicky, so I won't guarantee they will love it, but it's worth a try.

- ☐ 9 ounces chicken legs with skin and bone (use bone if feeding raw, remove bone and use meat and skin if cooking or finely grind the bone so there are no sharp pieces)
- ☐ 6 ounces chicken hearts
- ☐ 4 eggs
- ☐ 5 ounces pork muscle meat (95% lean)
- ☐ 4 ounces chicken liver
- ☐ 3 ounces mussels
- ☐ 2 ounces butternut squash
- ☐ 3 teaspoons ground flaxseed
- ☐ 2 teaspoons ground turmeric

If not using bone, add 1 tsp finely ground eggshell or organic eggshell powder for calcium requirements. An average 10-pound cat will eat 4 to 6 ounces per day. Food should be served warm, not cold out of the refrigerator. Food can be stored in the refrigerator for up to four days; freeze in small portions any food that cannot be fed within that time.

Superfoods to Improve Your Pet's Diet

You can improve your pet's health and longevity by adding some "superfoods" to their daily diet. The term superfood achieved the distinction of being added to the Merriam Webster dictionary in 2014 and is defined as "a food (such as salmon, broccoli, or blueberries) that is rich in compounds (such as antioxidants, fiber, or fatty acids) considered beneficial to a person's health. This list includes some of my favorites.

1. Fresh wild-caught fish (salmon or cod)—Fish is loaded with naturally anti-inflammatory omega-3 fatty acids that support heart, joint, skin, and brain health. Fish is also high in vitamin D, a fat-soluble vitamin that degrades quickly in processed food that is stored for long periods. Canned sardines in water can be used for these same benefits.

2. Fresh berries—Blueberries and cranberries contain polyphenols which are powerful antioxidants that destroy inflammation-causing free radicals in the body. They can inhibit tumor growth, lower blood sugar, and decrease chronic inflammation. Anthocyanins in berries improve cognitive (brain) skills. Cranberries help prevent E. coli bacteria from sticking to the bladder wall, reducing urinary tract infections. Berries should be smashed or ground for easier digestion.

3. Mushrooms—These are best served cooked; steamed or sauteed in coconut or olive oil. Mushrooms contain compounds that have been proven to have antiviral, antibacterial, and antitumor properties. They provide an excellent source of fiber for the good bacteria in the gut, improving the immune system. They help lower cholesterol and regulate blood sugar. They are particularly

useful for senior pets with muscle weakness or cardiac problems, as supportive care for pets with Cushing's disease, and for pets with viral diseases that compromise the immune system (Feline Immunodeficiency Virus, Feline Infectious Peritonitis, Feline Leukemia Virus, and viral papillomas for example). Shiitake is one of my favorite mushroom species. Dried mushrooms or mushroom powder can also be used, particularly for harder to find varieties such as Reishi, Maitaki, Turkey Tail, Lion's Mane, Tremella, and Chaga.

4. Bone broth—Contains glucosamine and chondroitin which support joint health and help slow the progression of degenerative joint diseases. Rich in amino acids, it can also be used during recovery after illness or surgery. Bone broth helps heal leaky gut and decrease inflammation in the digestive tract.

5. Dark leafy greens—A 2005 study showed that dogs who ate green leafy vegetables had a 90% reduction in their risk of developing cancer. Greens such as spinach and kale are rich in phytonutrients that give them antioxidant and anti-inflammatory qualities. They are high in calcium, iron, potassium, and vitamins A, C, and K. They are particularly useful for pets that have liver disease or anemia. Greens should be processed in some way to break down the plant cell walls—chopping, grinding, or cooking will accomplish this.

6. Eggs—Provide high-quality protein and fat-soluble vitamins A, D, E, and K. One egg will supply about 75 calories. Eggs can be fed raw or cooked.

7. Ginger—Helps fight cancer and relieve arthritis. Ginger soothes the digestive system and decreases nausea.

Ginger tea or cookies can be fed before transportation to decrease motion sickness or at bedtime to help settle a "grumbly" tummy. Ginger can also be added to meals, preferably fresh-grated root. Add ¼ to ½ teaspoon for small and medium dogs, up to 1 teaspoon for large dogs.

8. Turmeric—Curcumin is the active ingredient that is responsible for the antioxidant, anti-inflammatory, antiviral, antibacterial, and antifungal properties of turmeric. Turmeric is used to improve arthritis symptoms and to fight cancer. Absorption is enhanced when turmeric is made into Golden Paste by combining it with black pepper, cinnamon, and an oil or bone broth. I prefer making it with coconut oil.

9. Pumpkin—Rich in beta-carotene which enhances immune health and strengthens the eyes. Pumpkin is a great source of soluble and insoluble fiber which helps regulate bowel function. Canned or fresh pumpkin can be used.

10. Raw local honey—Honey contains minute amounts of local pollen, which helps increase the body's tolerance of it when exposed to larger amounts. The natural sugar in honey is fine for pets to ingest. Give ¼ teaspoon per 20 pounds body weight daily. Honey is soothing to the throat and very useful for treating a cough. Raw honey can be used topically to treat cuts and wounds, as it has bacteria-fighting properties (Manuka honey with a high UMF factor is best for wound healing). Honey should not be fed to immature animals, only to adult animals, as it may contain small amounts of Clostridium botulinum spores.

21

Treats as Part of the Diet

Treats are not a necessary part of the diet, but it is enjoyable to give rewards and special goodies to strengthen the human-animal bond. Treats should not make up more than a small percentage of the total daily caloric intake unless they are providing nutritional benefits; the extra calories should be subtracted from the daily meals.

Store-bought treats containing wheat, soy, artificial colors and flavorings, sugar, toxic preservatives, or high fructose syrup should not be fed. Use whole foods such as fresh or frozen berries, apples, pears, bananas, green beans, or broccoli (no grapes or raisins). Make your own dehydrated pieces of meat, liver, or sweet potato by putting ¼- inch-thick pieces on a tray in the oven on the lowest heat overnight. Store them in sealed containers in the refrigerator or freezer.

Do not purchase dehydrated chicken jerky treats, unless you know they were made from responsibly sourced meats. Jerky treats from China have been responsible for the illness and death of thousands of dogs in the past decade. The FDA was not able to identify the toxic principle in these treats, but they did finally publish a statement urging pet owners to avoid feeding them. They closed the investigation without providing answers for pet parents.

There are many recipes available to make your own biscuits and treats using simple ingredients. If your pet has a specific food intolerance you can control what goes into the treats. If possible, use organic, locally sourced, fresh whole ingredients.

GREEN MACHINE IMMUNE BOOST AND LIVER DETOX COOKIES

- ☐ 3/4 cup organic coconut flour
- ☐ 1/4 cup organic (No Sugar Added) sunflower butter
- ☐ 2 organic eggs
- ☐ 1/4 cup organic coconut oil
- ☐ 1/2 cup organic canned pumpkin
- ☐ 1 Tbsp chlorella or green superfood powder

DIGESTIVE AID COOKIES

- ☐ ¾ cup organic coconut flour
- ☐ ¼ cup almond butter that is made with only almonds—no sweeteners, xylitol, or added ingredients (substitute with sesame or sunflower if allergic to nuts)
- ☐ 2 organic eggs
- ☐ ¼ cup organic coconut oil
- ☐ ½ cup organic canned pumpkin
- ☐ 1 Tbsp organic Ceylon cinnamon
- ☐ 1 tsp organic dried ginger powder

Preheat the oven to 350. Combine all ingredients in a mixing bowl and form into a ball. Roll dough to ¼-inch thickness in between two sheets of parchment paper. (If the dough is too wet, add more flour. If dough is too dry, add another egg.) Use cookie cutters to cut dough into desired shapes. Alternatively, the dough can be rolled into balls ½ inch in diameter for baking. Transfer to a lined baking sheet. Bake for 12—15 minutes or until cookies are hard. Cool before serving.

22

Dental Care

By age three, most dogs and cats will have some degree of dental disease. Dental disease is a painful condition that occurs when bacteria, plaque, and tartar build up on the teeth and get trapped beneath the gum line. The bacteria can be absorbed into the bloodstream and wreak havoc on major organs throughout the body. Untreated dental infection can lead to heart valve disease, kidney disease, and even diabetes and cancer due to chronic inflammation and immune stress, not to mention the significant pain associated with dental infections and loose teeth. Early signs of dental disease in pets include bad breath, yellow tartar buildup on the teeth, and red and swollen gums. Early detection of your pet's dental disease is vital. If left untreated, it will progress to cause chronic pain and inflammation.

Some dogs and cats are genetically predisposed to dental disease.

Basepaws DNA testing for cats shows the chances that the cat will have periodontal disease, tooth resorptive lesions, and dental infections. Embark DNA testing for dogs checks for an inheritable condition called enamel hypoplasia. The results of these tests may motivate you to begin good oral hygiene in the early years and to be more vigilant if your pet is likely to have more dental disease problems.

There are four stages of periodontal disease. Periodontal disease is an inflammatory condition of the tissues that surround the teeth. Specifically, periodontal diseases are infections of the periodontal ligaments that hold the teeth in place, alveolar bone surrounding the teeth, and/or gum disease. If treated in the earlier stages, the disease can be treated and even reversed. More advanced stages often result in removal of the teeth.

- Stage 1: Gingivitis is caused by a buildup of plaque on the teeth. The plaque is formed as bacteria colonize on the surface of the tooth to form a biofilm. If left untreated, the biofilm will mineralize and produce a hardened calculus. The trapped bacteria under the gum line results in red and bleeding gums.
- Stage 2: Early periodontal disease is defined as 25% or less attachment loss between the teeth and gums. Radiographs will show early signs of the disease.
- Stage 3: With moderate periodontal disease, there is significant bone loss under the gum line. Tooth removal may be necessary at this stage; however, progression to Stage 4 can still be prevented with proper care.
- Stage 4: Cases of advanced periodontal disease have more than 50% gum retraction from the bone. Often, teeth will need to be extracted and a deep cleaning including scaling and root planning will be necessary.

The argument that pets need dry food to keep their teeth and gums healthy is a fallacy. The carbohydrates in dry pet food, which break down to sugars, contribute to dental disease. Sugar causes increased plaque and feeds the oral bacteria. Plaque leads to tartar, gingivitis, and periodontal disease. One study showed that dental health declined within just 17 days of switching from a raw to a kibble diet in dogs. Another study showed dental calculus was significantly higher in cats fed commercial diets versus feral cats eating wild prey.

The only way a dry food will help clean the teeth and gums is to feed a dry food specifically formulated in very large pieces with a large matrix that the pets must chew to break down to swallow. I do not recommend these diets however, because they are made with poor ingredients. Ingredients in one of these products include Brewers Rice (waste product of milling rice), whole grain corn (including the indigestible parts of the grain), chicken by-product meal (by-products, no real meat), powdered cellulose (fiber filler), soybean mill run (leftovers from processing soybeans), and flavoring. This is a very expensive product, made from cheap leftovers not fit for human (or in my opinion, pet) consumption.

The best way to prevent tartar and plaque on the teeth is by brushing, twice a day, every day, using organic coconut oil. The action of the brushing is the most important part of the procedure. Coconut oil can be mixed with species-appropriate probiotics to improve the bacterial microbiome in the mouth, helping reduce plaque and tartar buildup. Pet owners that begin dental care while puppies and kittens are young find it easier to establish a daily routine with a cooperative pet, however, some pets will not allow brushing and some owners cannot commit to brushing. Oral sprays, gels, and water additives are also available. Avoid water additives containing dyes or xylitol.

The Veterinary Oral Health Council shares a list of products that they claim will help decrease plaque and tartar accumulation, however the list is "sponsored", which means a price was paid to be on the list. Most of the products are made by big pet food companies using questionable ingredients (in my opinion). If you want to use a commercial dental product made for pets, avoid the following ingredients:

- glycerin
- sorbitol
- dyes
- alcohol
- chemical preservatives
- potassium sorbate
- zinc gluconate
- sodium benzoate
- polysorbate
- salt
- xylitol
- chlorhexidine
- paraben

Natural ways to work the teeth and gums include feeding raw meaty bones under supervision a few times a week. Pets fed raw diets or home prepared diets supplemented with raw meaty bones will have significantly less tartar. If your pet has never had raw meaty bones, be sure to research how to feed them. We offer a course on DrJudyU.com taught by Dr. Nick Thompson called *Bones and How to Feed Them*. Never feed cooked bones, as these are brittle and can splinter, causing broken teeth and bowel perforations.

Raw or cooked chicken or turkey gizzards also work well because they are lined by epichitin which is gritty and hard, removing plaque from the teeth when chewed. These are especially useful for cats.

Some pets will do well with chicken, turkey, or duck necks. Antlers are very hard; some dogs will break teeth chewing them. Ram horns are different from antlers. They are composed of compressed hair fibers, making them a bit softer and more digestible than antlers. They are often filled with marrow, which is an added health benefit.

Pets should be supervised when given any chew product. Check teeth for any damage after chewing. If the dog is an aggressive chewer, they are more likely to break teeth.

I have formulated a dental drop product that only requires application of a few drops to the gums and teeth, which is much easier to do than daily brushing. The drops help prevent plaque build-up and bad breath. The drops can also be mixed with coconut oil for brushing. Professional dental cleaning should be performed at the first signs of plaque or tartar build-up.

I am not a fan of the anesthetic-free dental cleanings. Much of the plaque is under the gumline, between, and behind teeth. Cleaning the inside surface of the teeth is extremely difficult in an animal that is not sedated. Removing plaque from teeth beneath the gumline is vital. In fact, it is even more important than scaling the portion of the teeth we can see. Bacteria thrive under the gumline, causing infections deep in the tooth root and jaw that can spread throughout the body and affect other organs, such as the heart and kidneys.

Without anesthesia, it is impossible to obtain X-rays to see what lies beneath your pet's gumline. **Radiographs are essential for diagnosing dental disease, as 75% of disease occurs below the gumline.** After examining dental radiographs of cats and dogs with teeth that appeared normal to the naked eye, veterinarians found 27.8% of dogs and 41.7% of cats had diseased teeth. In pets with abnormal-looking teeth, veterinarians found additional diseased teeth in 50% of dogs and 53% of cats. If you choose the anesthetic-free option for dental care, most likely you are just getting a cosmetic procedure.

Complications and deaths from anesthetic dental cleanings are uncommon in dogs and cats. Prior to the procedure, schedule a complete physical examination with your veterinarian. The exam should include listening to the heart, abdominal palpation, and an oral exam. Pre-op lab work is critical! If not already a standard part of the complete examination, request full lab work including a Complete Blood Count (CBC), Chemistry panel, and urinalysis. A thyroid blood test and chest x-rays are also recommended if your pet is middle aged or older. Based on the results of these tests, the anesthetic protocol can be adjusted based on the organ function of the animal. If a specialist (ex. Cardiologist) is regularly part of your pet's care team, schedule a pre-op exam with them as well. If your animal is considered at high risk for anesthesia, taking him/her to a veterinary dental specialist may be a safer option.

When dropping off your pet on the day of the procedure you will be asked to complete the hospital's admission forms. As part of the form packet, you will be asked whether you give a "red", "yellow", or "green" light for administering CPR in the rare event that your pet's heart stops during the procedure. It's important for your veterinarian to know your wishes before the procedure begins.

To prevent additional stress on your pet's immune system, do *not* give permission to administer vaccines on the day of the procedure. Acupuncture, cold laser, and removal of small lumps and bumps are safe to perform while your pet is under anesthesia for a dental cleaning.

At the start of the procedure, an IV catheter will be placed to administer intravenous fluids and medications. Intravenous fluids support the kidneys in processing the anesthesia and filtering it out of the body; fluids also help keep blood pressure stable. After administering fluids, an induction agent to sedate the animal will be administered intravenously. Once the sedation has taken effect, an endotracheal tube is inserted into the airway to administer gas anesthesia and oxygen and to prevent saliva and debris from the dental procedure from entering the airway and lungs.

During the procedure, your animal's vital signs will be monitored including blood pressure, body temperature, oxygen saturation, carbon dioxide levels, respiratory rate, heart rate, and electrical heart activity (EKG). Be sure to clarify with your veterinary team that this monitoring will take place by a qualified staff member.

Scaling (scraping away) tartar and plaque will be performed. Radiographs should be taken of every single tooth (clarify that this will be done). If extractions are needed, the animal may receive a nerve block. By adding a nerve block, the pet will experience less pain after the procedure. Deep root extractions will require sutures. The teeth are then polished to remove the scratches made on the teeth during scaling and planning. Scratches left on the surface of the enamel can invite tartar and plaque to adhere to the teeth more quickly.

When the procedure is finished, the gas anesthesia will be removed from your pet. When the care team has observed your pet sitting up and able to swallow, the endotracheal tube is removed. Vital signs will continue to be monitored until the pet is full awake and walking around, ready for discharge.

When you arrive to pick up your pet, you will be given discharge instructions as well as a report on number of extractions and after-care. Be sure to review the information with a member of the care team before you head home and get answers to any questions you may have. You may also receive prescribed medications for pain management and infection control. Ask questions about any side effects that may occur.

For the first 24 hours after the dental procedure, no solid food is recommended. A liquid diet of goat milk, congee, or bone broth would be appropriate. Pets may be nauseous from anesthesia and painful from the procedure. Do not give hard chews, bones, or hard treats for 7 to 10 days if sutures are present. Do NOT give any over-the-counter medications for pain. Veterinarians often prescribe NSAIDs (nonsteroidal anti-inflammatory drugs) for pain management. If giving an NSAID, watch for bloody or dark tarry stools; if they are present, STOP the medication immediately and call your veterinarian for alternative medication. Gastrointestinal ulceration is a serious side effect of this class of drugs. Natural alternatives to NSAIDS include:

- Herbal formulas such as Dog Gone Pain
- Homeopathic remedies include Arnica 1M and Hepar Sulphuris 200C twice daily for seven days or Arnica 1M and Hypericum 1M twice daily for 2 to 5 days if extensive work was performed
- If extensive bleeding occurs during the procedure, administer one dose of phosphorous 200C immediately following the procedure

Watch for signs of pain or infection: dropping food, flinching, tossing the head, aggression, increased drooling, blood in the saliva, halitosis, pawing at the face, swelling of the mouth and gums, or drainage or swelling around the eyes. These signs and behaviors can be a sign that a secondary infection is present.

Probiotics are important for recovery, especially if antibiotics are prescribed. A high-quality probiotic containing billions of CFUs and multiple strains is recommended. These can be started days in advance of the procedure if your animal does not regularly take a probiotic.

To detox the liver from the anesthesia, the following can be given to your pet one week before and two weeks after the procedure:

- Milk thistle: 100 mg per 20 pounds body weight twice daily
- NAC (N-acetyl cysteine): 250 mg per 30 pounds of body weight twice daily
- Sam-e (S-adenosyl-L-methionine): 90 to 425 mg based on size of pet once daily on an empty stomach
- B vitamins
- CoQ10: 5 to 10 mg per pound of body weight per day
- Foods with sulforaphane—broccoli, Brussels sprouts, kale. Broccoli sprouts—1/8 to ½ cup daily for ten days.

To detox the kidneys from the anesthesia, give your pet fresh or dried parsley. The dried parsley can be infused to make a tea. Another great herb is dandelion root or leaves. The leaves can be chopped or ground and added to food. Dried dandelion root and leaves are also available in powder and tea.

Other excellent supplements to use as your pet recovers from a dental procedure include:

- Golden Paste—¼ teaspoon per 10 pounds body weight twice daily
- Vitamin C—10 mg per pound body weight twice daily
- Spirulina—1/8 teaspoon per 20 pounds body weight twice daily

Proper dental care is one of the most important components to help your pet live a long, healthy, pain-free life. Don't ignore the teeth!

23

Natural First Aid Remedies

Pets and children have a way of finding trouble when you are least prepared. Having some supplies on hand may help avoid emergency veterinary visits or buy time to get the pet to the hospital for treatment.

In addition to avoiding a trip to the emergency hospital, you may also avoid having unnecessary medications and antibiotics prescribed for your pet. Antibiotics kill the offensive bacteria if appropriately prescribed, but they will also kill the good bacteria that are the most important aspect of maintaining a healthy immune system. Many times, natural therapies will be just as effective as pharmaceutical medications, without the side effects that may accompany their use.

First aid and Cardiopulmonary Resuscitation courses are available for pet owners both in-person and online. They are offered through the Red Cross and many private groups. The Red Cross has a free mobile application/app that provides veterinary as well as everyday pet care.

When making your own first aid kit for home or travel, there are many homeopathic and herbal remedies that can be included.

● **Toxin Ingestion**—In case of accidental ingestion of something you suspect may be toxic, it is best to call a poison control center to determine whether the pet needs veterinary care and whether inducing vomiting is recommended. Options include the United States ASPCA Poison Control Center, which is open 24 hours a day, 365 days a year. The phone number is (888) 426-4435. Another option is the Pet Poison Hotline, which is also open 24/7. The phone number is (855) 764-7661. Their website has an alphabetical listing of potential toxins for quick reference. Check resources within your country if you live outside the United States.

If the poison control center recommends inducing vomiting, hydrogen peroxide 3% solution works well for most pets. Hydrogen peroxide is an irritant to the pet's intestinal tract and typically works within 10 to 15 minutes, recovering about 50 percent of the ingested contents of the stomach. The vomiting can last for up to 45 minutes. The recommended dose is 1 teaspoon per ten pounds body weight. This dose can be repeated if the pet does not vomit within fifteen minutes. I have used this method numerous times with my dogs over the years.

Inducing vomiting can be dangerous in brachycephalic (short-faced) breeds because of concerns of causing aspiration pneumonia, so be sure to check with your veterinarian first. Do not induce vomiting if your pet is lethargic or comatose or if he is having seizures. If your pet ingested something more than two hours prior, it may be too late to induce vomiting.

- **Sprains, strains, and muscle aches**—Homeopathic arnica 30C can be given orally every few hours immediately after the injury. Moldable cold packs can also be placed over inflamed muscles or joints for ten minutes two to three times daily for the first 48 hours. After 48 hours change to warm packs to increase circulation and healing to the area. Herbal remedies are available; one of my favorites is Dog Gone Pain which can be used for cats or dogs. Chamomile, ginger, slippery elm bark, and turmeric (Golden Paste) can be given orally or applied as a poultice or as a liquid massaged onto the painful area.

- **Cuts, scrapes, wounds, and hotspots**—Manuka honey or virgin organic coconut oil act as natural antibacterial agents that will prevent infection. Colloidal silver can be very effective at decreasing inflammation and preventing infection. Aloe vera gel or an ointment containing lavender, yarrow, or calendula will sooth and help heal wounds. Compresses of warm green or black tea or chamomile tea can help decrease swelling.

    Hydrogen peroxide is not recommended for use on wounds, as it does not distinguish between good and bad cells within the wound. It kills everything, including the white blood cells that ward off infection, which slows down healing, making the wound stay open longer, which can lead to more infections.

    Another commonly used product for cleaning wounds is rubbing alcohol. While it is true that alcohol can work to minimize germ activity within the wound surface, it will also burn the skin immediately. Skin cells can be damaged, and the process is painful for your pet.

The first choice for cleaning a wound should be thorough flushing of water or saline over the injury to initially minimize infection. This will provide moisture and help cleanse the injury without risk of cell damage. Saline, when made correctly, has the same makeup as body tissue and is gentle on vital healing cells. Daily flushing will remove bacteria, pus, and dead cells.

To make a saline solution for your dog or cat, add ½ teaspoon of sea salt to one cup of boiling water. Stir to dissolve; use when cool. Make a fresh solution each time you need it.

- **For wounds that are bleeding**—powdered goldenseal or yarrow are very effective. Witch hazel also works to constrict blood vessels and is a good disinfectant for the wound. In a pinch, cornstarch or regular flour will work well. If bleeding is excessive, contact your veterinarian immediately.

- **Insect and spider bites**—can cause allergic reactions that may be life-threatening. Facial swelling or swelling of the ears may be the first sign that an allergic reaction is occurring. Severe reaction may result in coughing, wheezing, vomiting, diarrhea, or collapse. Symptoms typically occur within 30 to 60 minutes after the sting, however, in rare situations they can occur hours afterward, so it is important to keep a close eye on your pet all day.

  If your pet received a single sting somewhere on the body other than the mouth or muzzle and is not displaying any concerning signs, it is safe to monitor and care for their symptoms at home. Ice packs can be applied at the site of the sting and witch hazel is effective at decreasing pain when applied topically. A natural anti-inflammatory and antihistamine such as quercetin can be given orally. The dose is 5 to 10 mg per pound of body weight given twice daily one hour before or three hours after meals. One dose of the homeopathic Apis 30C may also be given.

If you notice any concerning signs or if your pet was stung multiple times or has had a bad reaction to a sting previously, you should take him to your veterinarian as soon as possible. Antihistamines are often prescribed for pets with a known history of allergic reactions; some may require steroids as well.

- **For simple gastrointestinal upset**—Ginger, catnip, or chamomile tea, ginger cookies, or slippery elm can help decrease nausea. These can also be used prior to transportation if your pet suffers from motion sickness. For loose stools, bentonite clay and slippery elm can be very effective, along with a bland diet (see Chapter on Tummy Trouble). If there is any blood in the vomit or stool, consult your veterinarian immediately. Vomiting or diarrhea that is profuse or lasts more than one day warrants a veterinary visit.

- **For mild cough**—One quarter teaspoon per ten pounds body weight of Manuka honey (local honey will also work) or slippery elm given orally will soothe the mucous linings of the respiratory tract. Cool steam humidifiers or allowing the pet to rest in the bathroom with the shower running to create steam can help loosen secretions and decrease coughing.

- **Mild ear inflammation**—This can be treated with a 50:50 mixture of witch hazel and aloe vera. Fill the ear canal, massage the base of the ear, wiping away any debris and liquid that can be seen in the canal using a cotton ball. Do not use cotton swabs deep in the ear canal, as the tissue is very delicate and may be harmed by the abrasive action. Never use cleaners that contain hydrogen peroxide, water, or alcohol in the ears, even if prescribed by your veterinarian. Water leaves moisture in the ear canal which leads to bacterial growth; alcohol burns the sensitive tissue in the ear canal which can be extremely painful.

- **Seizures or agitation**—CBD oil can be helpful to calm an anxious or agitated pet. It has been used successfully for many pets that suffer with seizures. If a seizure lasts more than one minute the pet should be taken to an emergency hospital. Any pet that has seizures should be evaluated by their primary care veterinarian to determine the cause of the seizures. Protect pets from falling down the stairs or off furniture during a seizure.

Other supplies to keep on hand include:

- Tweezers to remove splinters
- A soft infant rectal thermometer (normal temperature should be 100 to 102 degrees F.)
- Water-based lubricant to lubricate thermometer
- Sterile cotton balls for cleaning wounds
- Non-adhesive pads to cover wounds
- Bandaging supplies may include sterile gauze pads, Ace bandages or self-adherent pet bandages, and sterile bandaging tape. Never apply bandages tightly.
- Clean towels

Hopefully, you will never be faced with a severe accident or injury with your pet. Being prepared with simple first aid supplies may help you avoid an expensive trip to the emergency hospital. Pets with any symptoms that do not clear quickly should be evaluated by a veterinarian.

Congratulations!

Congratulations on taking the steps necessary to raise your naturally healthy pet. My goal is to change what is accepted as "normal" for pet longevity. We have been trained to believe that twelve years is a good lifespan for dogs and fifteen years is an exceptional lifespan for cats. Ideally, dogs should have good quality of life until age twenty and cats until age thirty. I'm not just talking about longevity with lifespan; I'm also advocating for twenty to thirty years of "health span". Health span is the length of time your pet leads a healthy, exuberant life.

By minimizing vaccines and use of chemicals, along with feeding a species-appropriate diet, we can achieve these goals. Vaccines, chemicals, and poor-quality diet all contribute to inflammation. Inflammation is the root of all disease, including cancer.

Finding a veterinarian that supports your goals of using natural therapies, when possible, may be the most difficult part of your pet parenting journey. Don't settle for less than the best for your furry friend. Find a veterinarian that is open to conversation and does not make you feel guilty for wanting to raise your pet with natural therapies and a good diet. Your pet's veterinarian will play a very important role in their life; it is critical you find someone that makes both you and your pet feel comfortable.

By following the recommendations in this book, it is possible to raise pets that will not be plagued by allergies and chronic inflammatory diseases. Your veterinary bills will be much less than expected because your pet will not need to be treated for chronic digestive issues, itchy skin, and repeated infections. Some owners might complain about the increased cost of supplying a high-quality diet, but the savings in veterinary bills will more than make up for the funds spent on food.

There are thousands of educational resources available for pet parents wanting to learn more about keeping their pets healthy and happy. I would caution against following the mainstream narrative calling for the use of annual vaccinations, monthly application of pesticides, and feeding pet food that is essentially waste products from the human food industry. By reading this book you have opened your eyes to the world of natural pet care; hopefully you will continue to follow this path with your pets for decades to come.

Useful Resources

For more information on natural pet care, visit www.drjudymorgan.com

For more information on natural treatment of different diseases, see my book *From Needles to Natural: Learning Holistic Pet Care*

For more information on using food to heal disease, see my book *Yin & Yang Nutrition for Dogs: Maximizing Health with Whole Foods, Not Drugs*

To learn how to make home-prepared dog food, check out my online course https://www.drjudyu.com/offers/UojtrVmG/checkout

For more information on good brands of pet food and pet food recalls, visit www.truthaboutpetfood.com

To find a holistic veterinarian, visit www.AHVMA.org

For courses on natural pet care, visit www.drjudyu.com

For more courses and webinars on natural pet care visit https://civtedu.org/courses/pet-owners

For more information on using essential oils, visit https://oilyvet.com/

Index

185